Ken Russell is a London surveyor who lives in Kent. He is the Puzzle Editor of *Mensa*, a magazine issued free each month to Mensa's 20,000 UK members.

Philip Carter is a Yorkshire estimator and a Justice of the Peace. He is Puzzle Editor of the 'Mensa Puzzle Special Interest Group'.

The Mensa Puzzle Book
Volume 2

*Ken Russell
and
Philip Carter*

SPHERE BOOKS LIMITED

A SPHERE BOOK

First published by Sphere Books Ltd 1990

Copyright © 1990 by Ken Russell and Philip Carter
Reprinted 1991

Reproduced, printed and bound in Great Britain by
Cox & Wyman Ltd, Reading

ISBN 0 7474 0600 0

Sphere Books Ltd
A Division of
Macdonald & Co (Publishers) Ltd
Orbit House
1 New Fetter Lane
London EC4A 1AR
A member of Maxwell Macmillan Pergamon Publishing Corporation

Authors' Note

This book is dedicated to our wives, both named Barbara, who have given us their support and encouragement in our endeavour to compile new and interesting puzzles, and have checked out the answers.

We also wish to acknowledge the assistance and advice given to us by Victor Serebriakoff, the International President of Mensa, who is a great puzzle innovator. We are indebted too to Harold Gale, the Mensa Chief Executive, a prolific puzzle composer, and we wish to thank the members of the British Mensa Committee who gave permission for use of the Mensa name in the title.

What is Mensa?

Mensa is a unique society. It is, basically, a social club – but a social club different from others. The only qualification for membership is a high score on an intelligence test. One person in fifty should qualify for membership; these people will come from all walks of life and have a wide variety of interests and occupations.

Mensa is the Latin word for table: we are a round-table society where no one has special precedence. We fill a void for many intelligent people otherwise cut off from contact with other good minds – contact that is important to them, but elusive in modern society. Besides being an origin of many new friendships, we provide members with a receptive but critical audience on which to try out new ideas.

Mensa is protean: its most visible feature is its diversity. It crosses the often artificial barriers which separate people from each other. It recruits, not like other societies by persuading people to think as they do, or by searching for a particular narrow common interest, but by scientifically selecting people who are able to think for themselves. Yet, although there appears little common ground and little surface agreement between members, we find there is an underlying unity which gives an unexpected strength to the society.

Mensa has three aims: social contact between intelligent people; research in psychology and the social sciences; and the identification and fostering of human intelligence. Mensa is an international society; it has more than 85,000 members. We have members of almost every occupation – business people, clerks, doctors, editors, factory workers, farm labourers, housewives, lawyers, police officers, politicians, soldiers, scientists, students, teachers – and of almost every age.

Enquiries and applications to:

Mensa
FREEPOST
Wolverhampton WV2 1BR

Mensa International
15 The Ivories
6–8 Northampton Street
London N1 2HV

Puzzles

So that you don't inadvertently read the solution to the next puzzle while you are checking your answer, the solutions are in a different sequence from that of the puzzles.

Pathway

Find eight words each commencing with the central letter 'Z'. The words are in any direction in adjacent squares. Each letter is used once only.

G	B	P	E	L	H	N
I	N	M	P	P	I	Y
E	A	O	E	E	T	R
Z	W	U	(Z)	E	E	R
S	G	I	Y	O	N	O
T	G	G	G	I	E	P
A	R	U	A	L	T	H

These are the number of letters in each word:

1. 8
2. 8
3. 6
4. 8
5. 6
6. 6
7. 5
8. 9

Square

Divide the square into four identical sections. Each section must contain the same nine letters, which can be arranged into a familiar nine-letter word.

U	E	T	U	D	I
D	T	M	E	M	L
T	U	I	U	T	T
U	E	L	T	M	U
T	U	D	T	D	I
M	I	L	U	E	L

Word Power

The answers to the clues are to be found in the grid in letter order. They are all nine-letter words.

Example: Speaking off the cuff (clue) is ADLIBBING.

P	H	D	A	B	F	M	T	Q
U	O	D	A	E	A	U	E	H
F	L	T	S	R	A	R	R	P
I	I	E	A	D	I	F	S	E
J	C	C	B	R	L	A	S	S
A	R	B	Y	O	H	L	H	U
T	T	A	O	A	S	I	I	O
I	T	I	N	N	S	L	E	C
S	A	M	C	D	E	S	H	G

1. Dried leaves used as a drug *Marijuana*
2. Type of ox *Buffaloes*
3. Impairment of nerves *Paralysis*
4. Worshipping charms
5. To the 2nd power
6. Spoil
7. Step
8. Children's game *Hopscotch*

5

Logic

Find the next figure in this sequence:

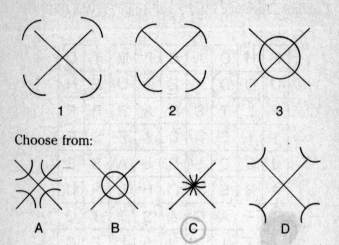

1   2   3

Choose from:

A   B   C   D

Labyrinth

Travel into each room once only to spell out a fifteen-letter word. You may move into the corridor as many times as you wish and you may start in any room, but you may visit each room once only.

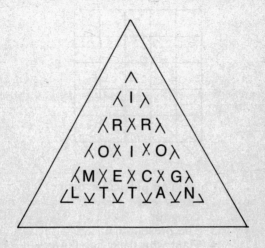

Magic Word Square

The answer to each of the five clues is a five-letter word. The five answers when fitted correctly into the grid will form a magic square where the words are the same when read horizontally or vertically.

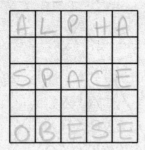

Clues: (no particular order)
1. Greek letter
2. Long for
3. The present age
4. Plant with daisy-like flowers
5. Excessively fat

8

Missing Letters

Solution 156

Supply the missing letters and find the table birds.

```
 1. * A * T * I * G *
 2. * H * A * A * T
 3. * O * D * I * E * N
 4. * U * K * Y
 5. * O * S *
 6. * O * D * O * K
 7. * U * K
 8. * R * U * E
 9. * U * L * T
10. * A * O *
```

Anagram Quotations

Solution 126

Work out the anagrams, each is a one-word answer, then fit the word into the correct quotation.

   (a) Nun she is   (b) I try Dave's
   (c) Mint moan code (d) Jude's price
   (e) Can centre dot   (f) Dip in fresh
   (g) I drain moat   (h) Peter Paul

1. . . . . . . is love without his wings. (*Byron*)
2. All . . . . . . makes a desert. (*Anon*)
3. Love is an . . . . . . which never wearies. (*Balzac*)
4. Patience is . . . . . . strength. (*Anon*)
5. A pleasing countenance is a silent . . . . . .

                                 (*Paul Duport*)

6. . . . . . . is not without comfort and hopes.

                                 (*Lord Bacon*)

7. In idleness there is . . . . . . despair. (*Carlyle*)
8. . . . . . . rule the vulgar. (*Voltaire*)

Pair-words

Solution 123

Pair a word from list A with a word from list B until you have eight pairs. There are two possible pairing words in list A for each word in list B and vice versa. There are two correct solutions.

List A	List B
Meat	Sweet
Foot	Apple
Core	Rugby
Tackle	Stirrup
Saddle	Stiletto
Sword	Lamb
Try	Sample
Toffee	Fish

No Repeat Letters

Solution 133

The grid below contains twenty-five different letters of the alphabet. What is the longest word which can be found by starting anywhere and working from square to square horizontally, vertically or diagonally and not repeating a letter?

C	K	W	N	H
Y	A	R	X	V
J	O	M	T	E
U	L	B	F	D
Q	S	P	I	G

Choice

Each number has a choice of three letters. Select the correct letters.

6	2	6	7	7	2	7
2		7		2		1
2	2	2	3	5	2	2
7		2		2		3
1	3	3	5	2	6	7
2		5		6		7
2	2	7	3	7	7	7

1	A	B	C
2	D	E	F
3	G	H	I
4	J	K	L
5	M	N	O
6	P	Q	R
7	S	T	U
8	V	W	X
9	Y	Z	

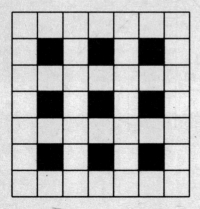

Spherical 1

Solution 40

Complete the word in each column – they all end in (S). The scrambled letters in the section to the right of each column are an anagram of a word: that word will give a clue to the word you are trying to find, to fit in the column.

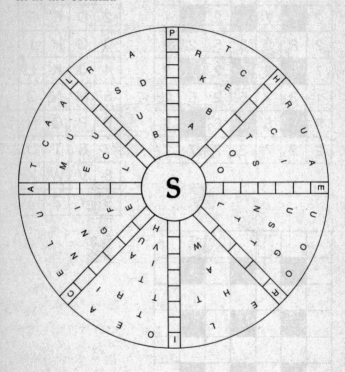

Acrostic

Here is a quotation from a book. Solve the clues and transfer the letters in the answers to the square grid where the quotation can be read. The name of the author will be seen in the vertical line.

1	2	3	4		5	6	7
	8		9	10	11	12	13
14	15		16	17		18	19
20	21	22		23	24		25
26	27	28		29	30		31
32	33	34	35	36	37	38	39
40	41	42		43	44	45	
46		47	48	49	50	51	
52	53	54		55	56	57	

Barbed fishing tool

Of two or more

Strange

Moved quickly

Vanished

Finished

Captain of robbers

Egg

Medicines

Numerous

Skin eruption

Shallow recess

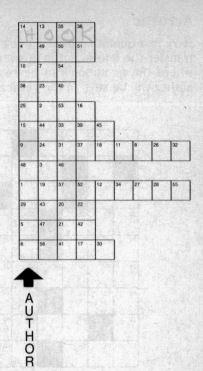

14	13	35	36					
4	49	50	51					
10	7	54						
38	23	40						
25	2	53	16					
15	44	33	39	45				
9	24	31	37	18	11	8	26	32
48	3	46						
1	19	57	52	12	34	27	28	55
29	43	20	22					
5	47	21	42					
6	56	41	17	30				

AUTHOR

Target

Pair up the thirty-two three-letter sections to form sixteen six-letter words.

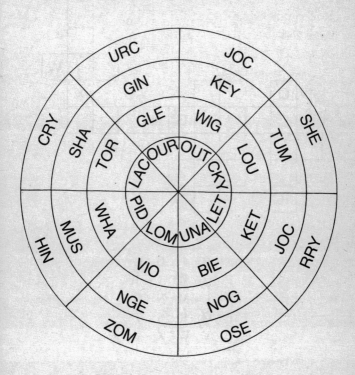

Alphabet Crossword

Fill in the remaining nineteen letters of the alphabet to complete the crossword.

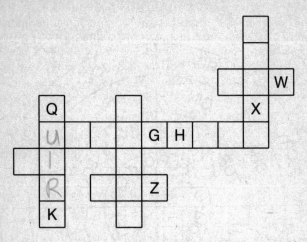

A-frame

Each horizontal and vertical line includes the consonants of a word which can be completed only by
adding the vowel 'A'. The two-digit number at the
end of each line indicates the number of consonants
and 'A' vowels. For instance, 42 stands for 4 consonants and 2 vowels.

Each letter in the grid is used once only, and all
the letters must be used.

	1	2	3	4	5	6	7	
1	K	T	P	R	M	S	L	42
2	T	N	S	L	V	S	P	32
3	K	R	K	S	N	N	S	53
4	C	D	K	R	W	W	R	52
5	T	X	G	S	S	H	S	42
6	R	Y	R	M	H	D	L	22
7	C	M	B	S	S	Y	P	41
	41	31	31	32	32	31	32	

Clues

Across
1. Connected with stars
2. Cease (naut.)
3. American state
4. Difficult
5. Dismayed
6. Native nurse
7. Chasm

Down
1. Fissure
2. Of the Isle of Man
3. Large enclosed piece
   of ground
4. Disturb
5. Gather
6. Small aggregate
7. Disgust

Trios

Solution 105

Some nine-letter words are made up of three three-letter words. For example: woebegone:WOE–BEG–ONE.

Use all of the three-letter words below once each only to form five nine-letter words.

EVE	GOT	ILL	LOP
MAN	PAN	PEN	RAM
RAN	RED	TAG	TEN
TOR	TRY	WAR	

Backwards and Forwards

Solution 85

A man is walking his dog on the lead towards home at a steady 4 m.p.h. When they are nine miles from home the man lets his dog off the lead. The dog immediately runs off towards home at 9 m.p.h. When the dog reaches the house it turns round and runs back to the man at the same speed. When it reaches the man it turns back for the house. This is repeated until the man gets home and lets in the dog. How many miles does the dog cover from being let off the lead to being let in the house?

Something in Common

Solution 23

What have the following in common?

WEAR
AXE
TEST
CROUCH
DART

Hexwords

Fit these words into the six spaces around each black centre, either clockwise or anti-clockwise, so that all the words link up.

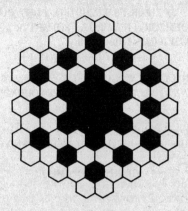

ROBUST
RUSTED
REVERT
TRIPOD
RETURN
BUTTER
PITTER
ROSTAS
TERROR
TAVERN
DETERS
STORED

Cryptograms

Solution 82

Each cryptogram is a straight substitution code, where one letter of the alphabet has been replaced by another. Each cryptogram is in a different code.

1. HA FI FITI CJJ ZHGIB PS XCZHD RQI EUFIT RU TICO ICDQ URQIT'V RQUMZQRV, H VMEEUVI RQI AHTVR IAAIDR FUMJO PI RU OHVVUJGI CJJ ATHIBOVQHEV.

    – PITRTCBO TMVVIJJ.

2. KL DILI IXNXOIXOTI NI N GVDHRLH YNH DILI N ZNYJJWIX – SWV IDJJWVX VNXKLV XKNH SWV OZZDYOHNXOWH.

    – NHGVLM ZNHC.

3. MEH GMMHIVM MB KBIQOPH AOCZBI GPZ VBAHT EGC BPRN TGTHRN QHHP CLKKHCCYLR GPZ MEHP BPRN YBT G CEBTM AEORH.

    – GRQHTM HOPCMHOP.

Farmer Giles

Solution 80

'How many livestock have you Farmer Giles?'
'All cows but four,' he replied
'All bulls but four,' he also replied.
'Have you any horses?'
'I have as many horses as cattle, not counting the chickens!'
'Have you many chickens?'
'I'm not sure how many chickens I have.'

How many livestock did Farmer Giles have?

Pyramid

Complete each line of the pyramid with a word beginning and ending with the letter 'A'. The words will match the eight clues provided, which are in no particular order.

1. Goat with long white silky hair
2. Fear of great heights
3. Distinctive air or quality
4. Turkish civil or military commander
5. Food of the gods in classical mythology
6. Areas in concert halls, theatres where audience sit
7. Place of public contest
8. Branch of mathematics

Word Search

Find the names of twenty flowers. They read across, down, diagonally, backwards and forwards, and always in a straight line.

D	L	I	L	A	C	M	U	E	G
A	C	O	W	S	L	I	P	L	O
I	L	W	O	T	E	N	A	Y	R
S	I	L	P	E	U	D	I	S	S
Y	L	S	I	R	I	L	A	N	E
X	Y	P	P	O	P	U	I	A	K
O	N	L	L	S	E	P	L	P	C
L	O	I	S	E	O	I	H	E	O
H	E	N	O	M	E	N	A	O	T
P	P	O	R	C	H	I	D	N	S

Prime Number

Eight balls numbered 1–8 are placed into a bag and then drawn out at random one by one and the digits written down to form an eight-digit number. What are the chances that the number so formed will be a prime number?

Knight's Move

Solution 8

Start at 'L' and by knight's moves spell out a quotation by Tennyson.

START

	S	M	H	E	L	F	L
U	T	N	D	N	E	T	E
A	N	T	R	A	I	O	H
N	T	T	O	S	F		H
I	N	G	H	A	E	A	O
U	O	M	H	O	Y	R	D
D	K	N	Y	O	I	K	P
G	A	T	N	I	P	A	E

Odd One Out

Solution 3

Which is the odd one out?

CUSTOMER
PROFITLESS
EVERYTHING
ORIGINAL
ASSIDUOUS

Blanks

This crossword has letters where the blanks should be. Fill in the blanks to make the crossword read correctly.

P	E	R	M	I	T	S	O	R	A	N	G	E
E	L	E	A	R	R	I	V	A	L	V	E	N
A	S	A	R	I	A	D	E	P	I	C	A	G
R	E	D	I	S	P	E	N	T	I	O	V	A
L	A	Z	E	S	S	C	S	S	B	R	I	G
S	T	E	M	S	A	L	E	S	O	N	C	E
T	A	N	B	O	N	A	N	Z	A	S	T	N
A	B	L	E	A	D	I	D	I	S	H	O	D
B	L	U	R	P	A	R	A	P	T	O	R	E
L	E	T	O	C	A	S	T	E	A	R	Y	E
A	L	E	W	E	R	U	U	P	O	N	O	M
Z	L	N	E	R	U	P	T	E	D	E	K	E
E	S	T	E	E	M	U	S	E	E	D	E	D

Anagram Theme

Arrange the fourteen words into pairs which give anagrams of seven words. The seven words produced will have a linking theme. For instance, if the words 'dial' and 'than' appeared on the list, they could be paired to form an anagram of 'Thailand' and the theme could be 'countries'.

AIL
AS
BEST
GENE
HEALS
HOPS
LANE
MAY
READ
ROPE
EDGE
SIP
SPIKE
TIN

Zoetrope

Find a three-letter word in the outer scale which will also give a three-letter word in the inner scale. Then find a four-letter word in both scales; and a five-letter word. The same letter may be used twice. For example, the letters WRY on the outer scale spell out NIP on the inner scale.

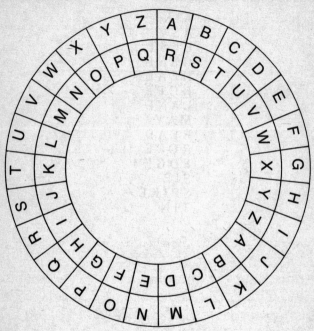

Square

Solution 2

Divide the square into four parts of equal size and shape. Each shape must include one of each of the four symbols.

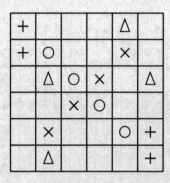

Something in Common

Solution 132

What have the following words in common?

ASS
ON
BOY
BIN
NAME
WAY

Pathway

Find eight words each commencing with the central letter 'X'. The words are in any direction in adjacent squares. Each letter is used once only.

H	I	S	U	H	O	I
T	N	C	S	T	P	D
N	E	A	Y	I	L	O
E	L	Y	(X)	Y	I	N
M	A	A	E	Y	L	T
O	N	C	B	O	O	E
H	T	E	E	N	H	P

These are the number of letters in each word:

1. 7
2. 8
3. 9
4. 5
5. 8
6. 6
7. 6
8. 7

Eiffel Tower

Solution 15

The height of the Eiffel Tower is 150 metres, plus half its own height. How high is the Eiffel Tower?

Grandpa's Party

Solution 78

My grandfather and his twin brother held a joint birthday party last week and invited their entire family. They both have an equal number of sons who, in turn, have as many sons as they have brothers, all surviving. The combined number of all these sons and grandsons is equal to the age of my grandfather, who in three years' time will be exactly three times my own age.

How old is my grandfather, how old am I, and how many grandsons received invitations to the party?

Fill in the square using the letter-groups below. They are in no particular order. The words read the same across and down.

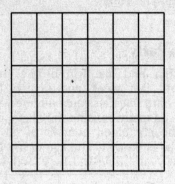

```
A T A R
R T S
S T A S
S T E
E R A R
A R E T
D E T
E D S
E S T
E R R
S E R
T U R
```

Colours

Start at the centre square and track from square to square horizontally, vertically and diagonally to find nine colours. Every letter is used once only. Finish at the top right-hand square.

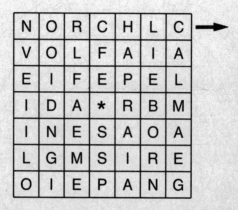

| N | O | R | C | H | L | C | →
|---|---|---|---|---|---|---|
| V | O | L | F | A | I | A |
| E | I | F | E | P | E | L |
| I | D | A | * | R | B | M |
| I | N | E | S | A | O | A |
| L | G | M | S | I | R | E |
| O | I | E | P | A | N | G |

Target Crossword

Find sixteen six-letter words by pairing up the thirty-two three-letter bits.

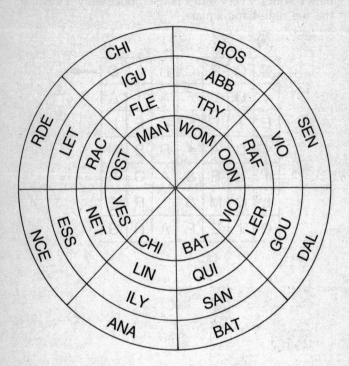

Choice

Solution 110

Each number has a choice of three-letters. Select the correct letters.

5	2	5	2	3	1	1	5	7
3		2		5		8		2
7	8	2	1	7		1	8	4
1			6	5	1	7		2
6	5	4	2		1	7	5	5
2		5	1	7	7			2
1	6	1		1	7	7	2	7
5		7		3		2		6
7	2	5	6	5	6	1	6	9

1	A	B	C
2	D	E	F
3	G	H	I
4	J	K	L
5	M	N	O
6	P	Q	R
7	S	T	U
8	V	W	X
9	Y	Z	

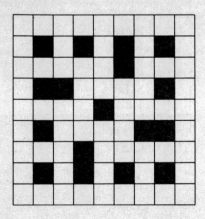

Keywords

Solution 10

1. I am nine letters long 123456789,
   My 23456 is a name,
   My 1234 is impudence,
   My 789 is an attempt.
   What am I?

2. I am eight letters long 12345678,
   My 123 is constructed from me,
   My 1234 is a comrade,
   My 5678 may buy me in Iran.
   What am I?

Fours

Solution 7

Find a four-letter word which when placed on the end of the first word produces another word, and when placed on the front of the second word also produces another word.

1.	STAR	* * * *	NESS
2.	PLAY	* * * *	WARD
3.	NINE	* * * *	AWAY
4.	MUSK	* * * *	BUSH
5.	OVER	* * * *	ROOM
6.	PART	* * * *	STEP
7.	PENT	* * * *	TILE
8.	PLAY	* * * *	LOTS
9.	RAIN	* * * *	HOOK
10.	SILK	* * * *	CAST

End

Solution 139

Twenty-six cards, each featuring a different letter of the alphabet, are placed face down on a table and then turned over at random one by one. What are the chances that the final three cards to be turned over will spell out the word 'END'?

Magic Squares

Solution 122

Ten words have been mixed up. Find out which words go into which grid and fit them in. The words read the same across and down.

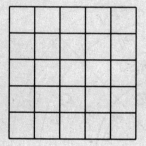
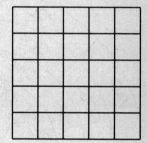

```
A G A P E
D A L E S
M E D A L
M O T O R
N O M A D
O K A P I
O M E G A
O P I N E
R I T E S
T A C I T
```

Three Words

Solution 42

What do these three words have in common?

FEED
TRUST
MOON

Target

Solution 134

Pair up the thirty-two three-letter sections to make up sixteen six-letter words.

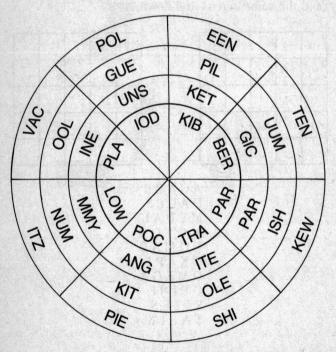

Acrostic

Here is a quotation from a book. Solve the clues and transfer the letters in the answers to the square grid where the quotation can be read. The name of the author will be seen in the vertical line.

	1	2		3	4		5	6
7		8	9	10	11	12		13
14	15	16	17	18	19		20	21
22	23		24	25	26	27		28
29	30	31	32	33	34	35	36	
37	38	39	40	41		42	43	44
45		46	47	48		49	50	51
52		53	54	55		56	57	58
59	60		61	62	63	64		

Requires

Hurting

Strike with whip

Accordingly

Engrave

Decays

Sketched

Clear sky

Peer

Insect

Type of meat

Small pointed tool

Plunders

Call up

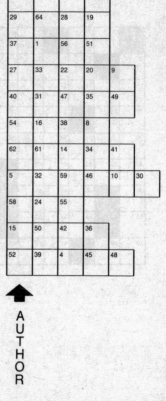

11	6	3	13	60	
53	44	57	25	7	18
26	43	63	21		
23	2	17	12		
29	64	28	19		
37	1	56	51		
27	33	22	20	9	
40	31	47	35	49	
54	16	38	8		
62	61	14	34	41	
5	32	59	46	10	30
58	24	55			
15	50	42	36		
52	39	4	45	48	

AUTHOR

Logic

Find the next figure in this sequence:

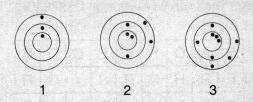

1   2   3

Choose from:

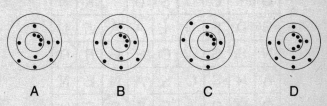

A   B   C   D

Word Power

The answers to the clues are to be found in the grid in letter order. They are all nine-letter words.

Example: The osprey (clue) is an OSSIFRAGE.

S	A	O	S	F	F	C	D	R
E	R	H	N	R	S	I	O	R
P	I	R	S	V	W	I	A	E
O	I	C	D	S	U	I	K	N
E	D	F	H	I	A	A	W	L
N	S	S	W	C	E	E	R	R
A	H	S	O	K	A	N	E	N
O	R	R	I	E	E	G	S	D
N	T	S	E	E	E	E	S	R

1. Stewed meat
2. Pottery
3. Tomb
4. Deodorant
5. Glove material
6. Disorderly action
7. Shares
8. Plant

40

Overlapping Words

Solution 47

Read clockwise to find the word in each circle. The number of letters in each word is indicated. You supply the missing letters.

Ten-letter

Ten-letter

Ten-letter

Eleven-letter

Eleven-letter

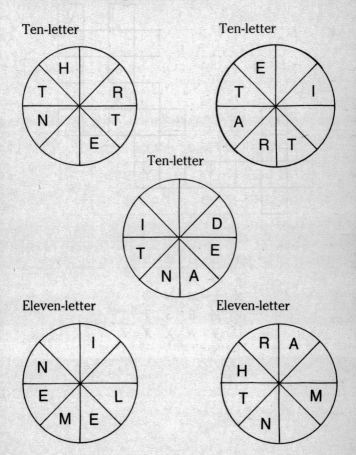

Alphabet Crossword

Fill in the remaining twenty-one letters of the alphabet to complete the crossword.

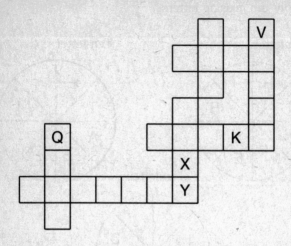

Odd One Out

Solution 51

Which is the odd one out?

> FACETIOUS
> UNCOMPLIMENTARY
> EQUATION
> ABSTEMIOUS
> SUBCONTINENTAL

Labyrinth

Solution 37

Travel into each room once only to spell out a fifteen-letter word. You may move into the corridor as many times as you wish and you may start in any room.

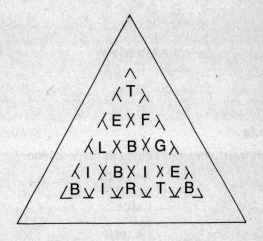

Sequence

Solution 45

Rug, oblate, yoghurt, goose, book, inkpot . . .

What word below completes the above sequence?

Skittle, vacant, paper, milk, Irish, debut.

Missing Letters

Solution 73

Supply the missing letter and find water in motion.

```
 1. * A * E * C * U * S *
 2. * T * E * M * E *
 3. * P * I * G
 4. * O * N * A * N
 5. * O * N *
 6. * R * B * T * R *
 7. * R * O * L * T
 8. * U * H * R
 9. * E * L
10. * A * E * W * Y
```

Words

Solution 28

Which word does not belong in this sequence?

APLOMB
BEATEN
CARD
ELF
GRAPH

Anagrams

1. Work of art (5–2–4).
   I LOVE MS NUDE.

2. Politician (6–6).
   LOAN ARRANGED.

3. Somewhere in America (10).
   AFRICA LION.

4. Animal (9).
   ORCHESTRA.

5. Somewhere in Africa (6–6).
   SEAR SAD EARTH.

Pair-words

Pair a word from list A with a word from list B until you have eight pairs. There are two possible pairing words in list A for each word in list B and vice versa. There are two correct solutions.

List A	List B
Goose	Swan
Gargoyle	Nets
Cricket	Fountain
Teapot	Slice
Pen	Match
Vesta	Quill
Golf	Caddy
Fish	Spout

Common Clues

Solution 35

What have all the answers to the following clues got in common?

1. Any substance used to impart colour
2. Powerful tractor
3. Give help
4. Close-quarters combat between fighting aircraft
5. Extensive disaster
6. Someone who shrinks from danger
7. The highest point
8. Peaked hat
9. Abashed
10. Ornamental shrub, also called Japonica

Word Search

Solution 65

You are looking for a certain word in this paragraph which occurs once only. The first letter of this word is the seventh after a vowel and this vowel is letter number seven to appear after its last letter. What is the word?

Choice Crossword

Each number has a choice of three letters. Select the correct letters.

2	2	1	3	2	2	7
2	■	1	■	3	■	2
6	2	8	3	7	2	2
3	■	5	■	6	■	1
7	2	6	8	1	5	7
2	■	7	■	3	■	2
2	2	7	2	6	7	7

1	A	B	C
2	D	E	F
3	G	H	I
4	J	K	L
5	M	N	O
6	P	Q	R
7	S	T	U
8	V	W	X
9	Y	Z	

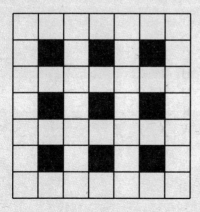

Alphabet Crossword

Fill in the remaining twenty-two letters of the alphabet to complete the crossword.

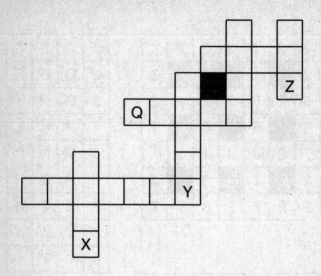

A B C D E
F G H I J
K L M N O
P Ø R S T
U V W X̶ Y̶ Z̶

48

Square Words

Travel clockwise round the perimeter of each square and finish at the centre to spell out the nine-letter words. Each word starts at a corner square. You supply the missing letters.

	E	T
A	A	E
C		R

	A	M
L	E	
	O	O

E	R	
		H
O	L	E

	E	P
N		R
E		E

	A	N
L	E	
P		A

E-Frame

Each horizontal and vertical line includes the consonants of a word which can be completed only by adding the vowel 'E'. The two-digit number at the end of each line indicates the number of consonants and 'E' vowels. For instance, 42 stands for 4 consonants and 2 vowels.

Each letter in the grid is used once only, and all the letters must be used.

	1	2	3	4	5	6	7	
1	S	X	S	T	V	T	F	42
2	N	R	V	L	N	S	R	22
3	T	T	L	C	F	V	F	42
4	V	N	N	T	S	L	R	33
5	C	N	L	C	S	R	S	32
6	S	T	P	M	S	S	C	31
7	L	T	X	T	L	R	N	33
	42	32	42	32	54	33	54	

Clues

Across
1. Musical group
2. Level
3. Accomplish
4. Number
5. Town in Germany
6. Hotchpotch
7. Stagger

Down
1. Choose
2. Go in
3. Go out
4. Select for office
5. Morning tea
6. Harsh
7. Compliance

Division

Solution 90

Arrange the following digits, 1–2–3–4–5–6–7–8–9, to form a single fraction that equals one eighth.

Vowels

Solution 53

Find a seven-letter word in the English language which contains the five vowels, A, E, I, O, U, once each only (but not in the correct order).

Elimination

The answers to the twelve questions are found by pairing off twenty-four of the twenty-five words. You will then have one word over.

1. Rodent has great difficulty in walking?
2. Get the nag for a birthday present?
3. Night worker at the railway yard?
4. Give the rough player his marching orders at hockey?
5. Student makes a pass at College?
6. Does this bird play a tune at the seaside?
7. Search for the warlock.
8. Does his mouth light up when it gets dark?
9. You will find him at the wicket but not in the dark.
10. The pilot will have to avoid the topiary artist.
11. This tree is not liked by chimpanzees.
12. This musical instrument is good value.

Select from

1. Bandi	13. Lantern
2. Bogey	14. Monkey
3. Bully	15. Man
4. Coot	16. Man
5. Fresh	17. Night
6. Gift	18. Off
7. Golly	19. Penny
8. Hedge	20. Piper
9. Horse	21. Puzzle
10. Hunt	22. Sand
11. Hopper	23. Witch
12. Jawed	24. Watchman
	25. Whistle

Hexwords

Fit these words into the six spaces around each black centre, either clockwise or anti-clockwise, so that all the words link up.

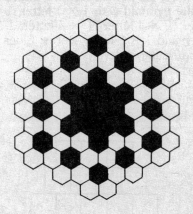

DEBUTS
TUMOUR
BURSAR
PARADE
DONATE
NETTLE
NEBULA
RACOON
MELODY
LEASES
BOOMED
TUREEN

Pyramid Quotation

'I can resist everything except temptation'

– Oscar Wilde

Using all thirty-six letters of the above quotation complete the pyramid with 1 × 1-letter, 1 × 2-letter, 1 × 3-letter, 1 × 4-letter, 1 × 5-letter, 1 × 6-letter, 1 × 7-letter and 1 × 8-letter words. Clues are given, but in no particular order.

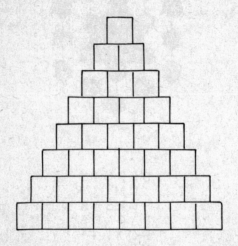

Clues
- Attempt
- Systematic plan for course of action
- Small, petty
- The pronoun of the first person singular
- Make hole by digging
- Colour, tinge
- To move or proceed
- Type of bowler at cricket

Double Crossword

Place the words into crosswords. The crosswords have been mixed up.

ARE	SEPT	FARCE
ICE	USER	BUGLE
INN	BLEW	ALIEN
OIL	COTE	FETED
AVE	RARE	
SPY	ANTE	
LOW	ALES	MALFORMED
EBB	CROW	PROMISARY
LAG	WEEP	TELEPHONE
IRE	CEDE	REMEDIATE
ERA	BLOB	
ODD	CABS	
AIL	TIRE	
ERA	ODES	
PER	SAFE	
EFT	EWER	
MEN	SPEW	
TIL	WADS	
OVA	TYRE	
ROE	CAMP	
ERE		
ROC		
NOB		
PIP		
ORE		
ROD		
EON		
TOR		

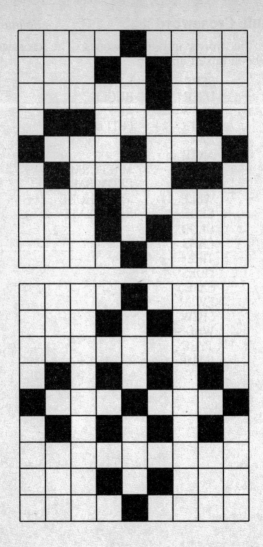

Pyramid

You must enter each room once only in a continuous route and spell out a fifteen-letter word. You may enter the corridor as many times as you wish.

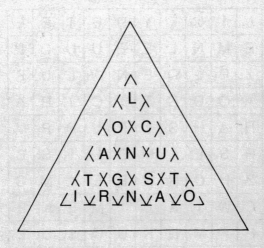

Word Search

Find the names of twenty-one trees. They read across, down, diagonally, backwards and forwards, and always in a straight line.

L	I	C	E	Y	D	B	T	E	E
E	M	N	L	E	E	U	U	C	L
Z	P	L	O	E	N	W	L	U	P
A	O	D	C	T	I	C	I	R	A
H	A	H	S	L	P	L	P	P	M
R	S	E	L	M	O	L	I	S	B
Z	H	O	R	N	B	E	A	M	C
C	W	I	A	L	I	M	E	N	E
P	F	M	N	K	U	O	I	U	E
O	R	A	N	G	E	N	L	T	H

Sequence

What pair of letters continue this sequence?

OE, TO, FE, TN, TY.

Knight's Move

Start at 'T' and by knight moves spell out a quotation by Sallost.

START

T		L	I	L	G	K	T
T	T	O	E	I	H	I	H
	S	H	A	N	S	S	E
I	E	F	D	U	D	I	K
I		R		P		T	E
M	S	N	R	T		E	
E	D	N	S		N	E	H
I	A	I	D	D	E		A

Connections

Insert the numbers nought to nine in the circles, so that for any particular circle the sum of the numbers in the circles connected directly to it equals the value corresponding to the number in that circle, as given in the list below.

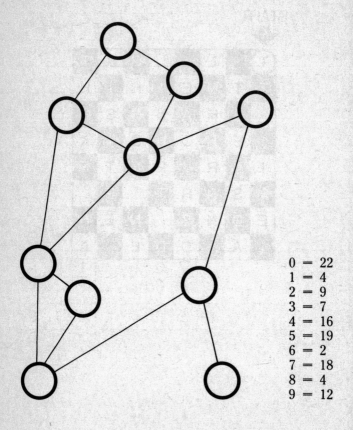

0 = 22
1 = 4
2 = 9
3 = 7
4 = 16
5 = 19
6 = 2
7 = 18
8 = 4
9 = 12

Blanks

This crossword has letters where the blanks should be. Fill in the blanks to make the crossword read correctly.

T	E	M	P	E	R	E	E	M	B	E	R	S
E	P	E	L	K	E	V	N	A	I	L	E	I
S	L	A	Y	E	D	E	A	C	T	O	R	S
T	A	G	S	D	A	N	C	E	S	P	E	T
E	C	R	U	M	B	U	T	S	C	E	D	E
R	E	E	L	S	O	N	I	B	I	D	A	R
A	R	C	C	O	D	A	M	U	D	D	Y	E
S	P	V	E	T	E	I	E	N	E	V	E	R
P	E	A	R	S	E	R	A	G	R	I	M	E
R	A	N	T	U	S	E	R	S	S	S	I	P
A	R	D	E	N	T	D	E	N	T	I	R	E
N	M	A	L	T	O	E	V	A	I	T	I	L
G	A	L	L	O	P	E	E	G	E	S	T	S

Anagrammed Synonyms

In each of the following, study the list of three words. Your task is to find two of the three words which can be paired to form an anagram of one word which is a synonym of the word remaining. For example:

LEG – MEEK – NET

The words 'leg' and 'net' are an anagram of 'gentle' which is a synonym of the word remaining 'meek'.

1. HUNT – CRONE – CLUB
2. CLOSE – MINE – MINT
3. NOISE – RID – SCORN
4. ART – PELT – DISH
5. RIM – RED – ROB
6. DEED – EMPTY – REST
7. SEE – HOME – CINDER
8. MANNER – GREAT – ORDER
9. CUT – CLEAR – EAT
10. REMIT – STOP – NEAT
11. DOSE – NUDE – BIRD
12. APE – PRY – ADO
13. LIE – ITEM – CART
14. RIP – MAR – AIM

Double Crossword

Place the words into crosswords. The crosswords have been mixed up.

LAX	FEEL	AGREE	MALAISE	REGULATOR
ART	USER	TONIC	BALANCE	DEODORANT
AWE	EARN	LARVA		DISSENTER
ANT	AFAR	TINGE		TRAVELLER
ILL	EPEE	EXTRA		
EAR	KNEE	OCCUR		
SAC	STAB	SEDAN		
ORE	YETI	PRINT		
DON	FLAY			
OWE	STAY			
NET	ANTE			
ARE	BEEN			
TOR	SNAG			
ONE	OGLE			
NOG	FEEL			
AIR	AREA			

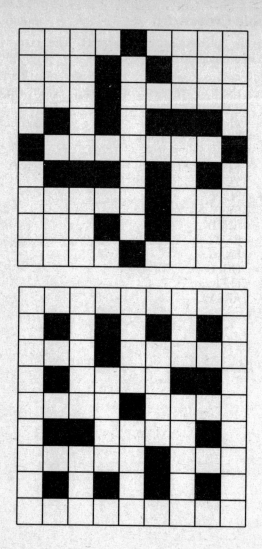

Zoetrope

Find a three-letter word in the outer scale which will also give a three-letter word in the inner scale. Then find a four-letter word in both scales; and then a five-letter word. For example, the letters LAP on the outer scale spell out APE on the inner scale.

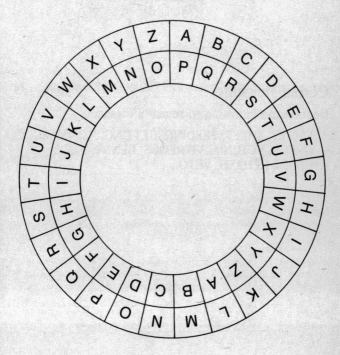

Odd One Out

Solution 127

Which is the odd one out?

> EXCUSE
> PREVENT
> USE
> PRESENT
> WOUND

Coded Message

Solution 145

Decode the following to reveal a message:

EMPTY, SHEET, FEEDING, BETTING, FEMINISM, GREEN, PETUNIA, VITREOUS, BENNY, VEIL, BEGIN, REHASH, VETO.

Square

Divide the square into four parts of equal size and shape and each shape to include one of each of the four symbols.

		+			O
O	×			△	
O		×	△		
	+	△	×	+	
	△		+	×	O

Pathway

Find eight words each commencing with the central letter 'V'. The words are in any direction in adjacent squares. Each letter is used once only.

D	I	O	S	E	D	D
I	R	C	E	T	N	E
A	V	A	O	E	T	T
O	N	I	(V)	E	L	A
Y	R	E	I	U	C	O
T	I	S	E	L	I	T
S	O	C	N	I	P	Y

These are the number of letters in each word:

1. 8
2. 8
3. 6
4. 8
5. 7
6. 9
7. 5
8. 5

Beads

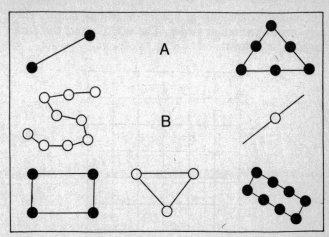

From the choice below choose the beads which should be correctly placed in positions A and B.

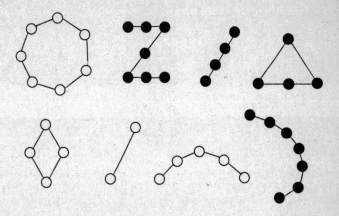

6 × 6 Magic Square

Fill in the square using the letter groups below. They are in no particular order. The words read the same across and down.

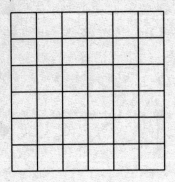

```
C R E
C L E
E E M
L U S
A T E
R U S
E S T
I C A
C I R
R A R
E S T
T R E
```

Nines

When the sum of the digits of a number will divide exactly by nine, then the number itself will also divide by nine – for example, 2673 : 2 + 6 + 7 + 3 = 18. With this in mind, place the digits into the grid so that each horizontal and vertical line, when read both forwards and backwards, will divide exactly by nine.

1, 1, 1, 1, 1.
2, 2, 2, 2.
3, 3, 3, 3, 3, 3.
4, 4, 4.
5.
6, 6, 6.
7.
8.
9.

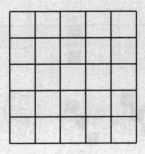

Crossword Fill-in

Solution 148

Place the 3 × 3 sets in the grid to complete the crossword.

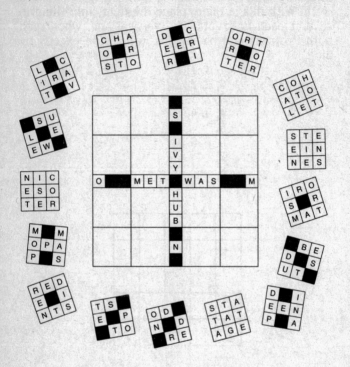

Spherical 2

Complete the word in each column – they all end in 'S'. The scrambled letters in the section to the right of each column are an anagram of a word: that word will give a clue to the word you are trying to find to fit in the column.

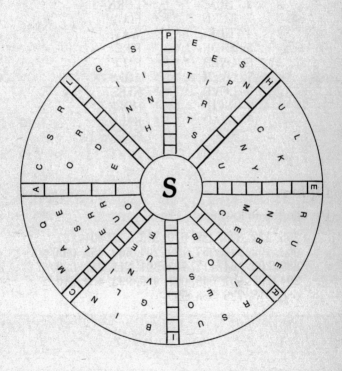

Fours

Solution 88

Find a four-letter word which, when placed on the end of the first word, produces another word, and when placed in front of the second word also produces another word.

1. WOOD   * * * *   WARD
2. TRUE   * * * *   LORN
3. TURN   * * * *   FLOW
4. TIDE   * * * *   WAYS
5. SHOE   * * * *   PIPE
6. OVER   * * * *   FALL
7. OVER   * * * *   AGES
8. LOVE   * * * *   NESS
9. INCH   * * * *   HOLE
10. GLAD   * * * *   BALL

Cipher

Solution 83

Decode the following:

265, 122, 838, 289, 010, 313, 113, 991, 867, 003, 102, 212, 937, 199, 204, 669, 453, 093, 889, 202, 104, 111, 753, 301, 311, 211, 030, 294, 707, 007, 648, 001, 929, 993, 408, 010, 668, 315, 726, 338, 559.

Magic Squares

Ten words have been mixed up. Find out which words go into which grid and fit them in. The words read the same across and down.

ACTOR
ALERT
APACE
ENTER
GORSE
LEERS
PAPAL
PASTE
STAGE
TALON

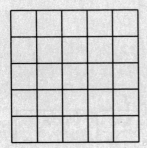

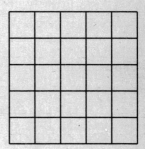

Advanced Matrix

Look along each line horizontally and down each line vertically and decide from the choice given what you think should logically be the missing tile.

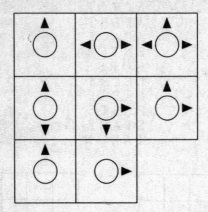

Choose from:

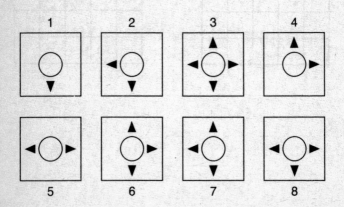

Target

Pair up the thirty-two three-letter sections to form sixteen six-letter words.

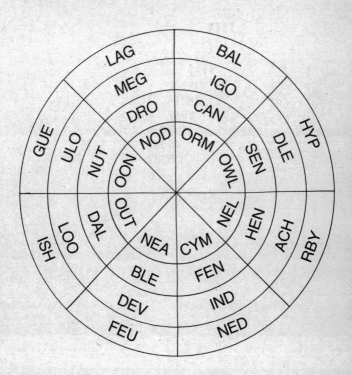

Numbers

Find a reason for arranging these numbers into four groups of three.

1012
1444
1649
1657
1787
2981
3821
3947
4530
4609
5362
7201

Choice

Solution 67

Each number has a choice of three letters. Select the correct letters to make up a crossword.

4	2	3		3		3	4	4
2		7	6	1	8	5		1
1	7		1	6	2		1	9
	5	2		1		5	5	
3	4	1	5	5	6	3	7	2
	1	7		7		7	5	
5	6		1	6	5		5	9
6		7	7	2	2	2		2
2	3	5		2		5	2	7

1	A	B	C
2	D	E	F
3	G	H	I
4	J	K	L
5	M	N	O
6	P	Q	R
7	S	T	U
8	V	W	X
9	Y	Z	

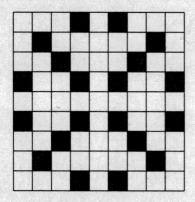

Word Circle

In the example, a ring of six-letter words, each over-lapping by two letters, is divided into two-letter groups and arranged in alphabetical order.

AN, ED, GL, IT, OR, PH gives the answer:
ANG**L**ED, **ED**ITOR, **OR**P**H**AN.

Now try to unscramble the letter-pairs below, to find a circle of eight six-letter words.

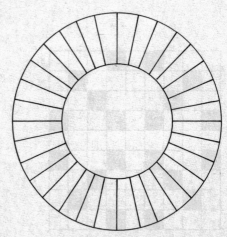

AP, AT, BR, CY,
EC, ER, ER, HY,
IC, ID, IO, MI,
NE, OT, PH, TH.

Word Power

The answers to the clues are to be found in the grid in letter order. They are all nine-letter words.

Example: an insect (clue) is a WOODLOUSE.

G	I	W	H	P	S	T	O	M
A	O	A	A	C	O	R	N	F
B	F	U	O	R	O	H	E	R
T	S	N	E	L	W	D	I	B
E	L	S	S	N	C	U	H	O
T	P	T	Y	H	S	O	C	N
K	E	R	U	O	O	L	I	A
D	L	O	A	R	S	V	O	I
E	Y	E	M	M	E	N	E	D

1. Short club
2. Whirlpool
3. Fastener
4. Bad weather
5. Attack
6. Fun and games
7. Fishlike
8. Fortification

81

Common Clues

Solution 151

What do all the answers to these clues have in common?
1. Large farm outbuilding
2. Wrench with turning action
3. Strike lightly
4. People in general
5. Plane geometric figure
6. Device for winding
7. Mechanical device for holding a component
8. Open armed conflict

Addition

Solution 68

In the addition sum below only one of the decimal points is in the correct position. Alter four of the decimal points to make the sum correct.

$$\begin{array}{r} 78.647 \\ 38.29 \\ 468.2 \\ 1.85 \\ \hline 8479.42 \end{array}$$

Labyrinth

Solution 154

Travel into each room once only to spell out a fifteen-letter word. You may move into the corridor as many times as you wish and you may start in any room, but you may visit each room once only.

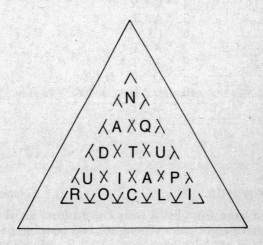

Missing Letters

Supply the missing letters and find pastry.

1. * H * R * B * E * D
2. * I * G * R * R * A *
3. * C * N *
4. * L * N
5. * A * T
6. * I *
7. * A * T *
8. * A * T *
9. * O * G * N * T
10. * U * N - * V * R

Pair-words

Pair a word from list A with a word from list B until you have eight pairs. There are two possible pairing words in list A for each word in list B and vice versa. There are two correct solutions.

List A	List B
Palm	Month
Moon	Mickey
Mouse	Cane
Sugar	Trap
Twig	Date
Calendar	Rum
Pluto	Planet
Gin	Tree

Book Titles

Solution 33

Each book title is the clue to a word. The author's name is an anagram of the word you are looking for. For example: THE WRITER by A. Routh. Answer: AUTHOR

1. HOLD SPELLBOUND by Len Hart
2. COWARDLY CONDUCT by May Lunn
3. RENEGADE by E.N. Carter
4. SIMPLE HAIRSTYLE by Sid H. Kane
5. THE OLDEST PARTY by D. Steel
6. BEAMING WITH JOY by Ian Dart
7. SUGAR by Gus Cole
8. OLD AND FEEBLE by Ted Price
9. THE GEORGE FORMBY STORY by Luke Lee
10. SMALL EXHIBITION by Sid S. Howe
11. IDENTITY CONFUSION by Sam E. Kane
12. SHORT OF WIND by Albert Hess
13. MILITARY COMMAND by Al Green
14. PASS BY by A. Sleep
15. DIFFICULT TO OVERCOME by Mable I. Ford
16. CULTIVATED LAND by N. Grade

Detective Work

Solution 125

Four suspects, Jack Black, Sid Dark, Alf Grey and Jim White, are being interviewed at the scene of a murder. Each of the suspects is asked a question to which their answers are given below. Only one of the answers is the truth. Who committed the murder?

Jack Black: 'Sid Dark committed the murder.'
Sid Dark: 'Jim White committed the murder.'
Alf Grey: 'I didn't commit the murder.'
Jim White: 'Sid Dark is lying.'

Choice Crossword

Each number has a choice of three letters. Select the correct letters.

6	2	2	7	7	2	2
2		3		7		2
7	3	7	7	7	2	7
3		7		2		3
6	5	7	5	2	2	6
2		4		2		2
7	4	1	5	2	2	6

1	A	B	C
2	D	E	F
3	G	H	I
4	J	K	L
5	M	N	O
6	P	Q	R
7	S	T	U
8	V	W	X
9	Y	Z	

Fore

Work from square to square vertically, horizontally or diagonally to find twenty-six words which can be prefixed with 'fore'. Squares may be used more than once, but not in the same word. There are no redundant squares.

L	B	S	E	E	S	O	L
L	C	E	R	N	L	I	L
E	W	A	M	T	C	G	A
T	N	O	S	D	H	T	S
A	G	D	R	F	T	R	U
L	E	A	N	D	E	E	O
H	O	U	H	H	A	G	C
C	K	R	G	T	F	I	N

Connections

Each pair of words, by meaning or association, leads to another word. Find the missing words 18–30. The number of letters in the missing word is indicated by the dots.

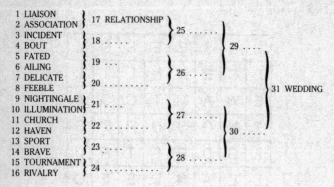

1 LIAISON
2 ASSOCIATION } 17 RELATIONSHIP
3 INCIDENT
4 BOUT } 18 . . . . .
5 FATED
6 AILING } 19 . . .
7 DELICATE
8 FEEBLE } 20 . . . .
9 NIGHTINGALE
10 ILLUMINATION } 21 . . . .
11 CHURCH
12 HAVEN } 22 . . . .
13 SPORT
14 BRAVE } 23 . . . .
15 TOURNAMENT
16 RIVALRY } 24 . . . .

25 . . . . . .
26 . . . .
27 . . . . . .
28 . . . .

29 . . . .
30 . . . . .

31 WEDDING

Alphabet Crossword

Solution 49

Fill in the remaining twenty-one letters of the alphabet to complete the crossword.

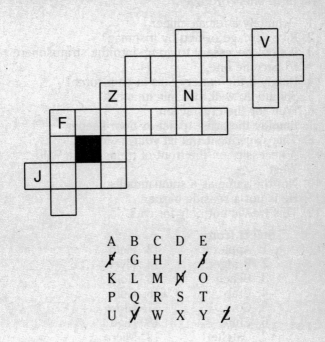

Inflation?

Solution 20

Why are 1990 fifty pence pieces worth more than 1989 fifty pence pieces?

Elimination

The answers to the twelve questions are found by pairing off twenty-four of the twenty-five words. You will have one word over.

1. Definitely a female miner.
2. Rice acreage owned by Irishman?
3. It's not necessary to go up into the stratosphere to become one.
4. Handy if the battery fails in your torch?
5. Should go well with minute steak?
6. Fruit for the crustacean.
7. Employ the artist to act as door-keeper.
8. This sweetmeat will fill your mouth.
9. A necessity on the front of trains in the Wild West.
10. Not the same as a somnambulist.
11. He is not a seaside barber.
12. This tree is not only for cats.

Select from

1. Apple	13. Field
2. Bridge	14. Flyer
3. Beach	15. Gold
4. Crab	16. Gob
5. Cow	17. Glow
6. Chip	18. High
7. Catcher	19. Micro
8. Comber	20. Paddy
9. Draw	21. Pussy
10. Dreamer	22. Stopper
11. Digger	23. Stream
12. Day	24. Worm
	25. Willow

Magic Square

The answer to each of the five clues is a five-letter word. The five answers when fitted correctly into the grid will form a magic square where the words are the same when read horizontally or vertically.

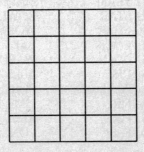

- The capital of Morocco
- To die away
- Anglo-Saxon land holder
- Devoid of intelligence
- Remove one's clothes

Fours

Find a four-letter word which, when placed on the end of the first word, produces another word, and when placed on the front of the second word also produces another word.

1.	TEAM	* * * *	MATE
2.	STAR	* * * *	BOWL
3.	CHAR	* * * *	WORM
4.	COCK	* * * *	BARS
5.	COME	* * * *	WARD
6.	DISC	* * * *	ALLS
7.	FILM	* * * *	PORT
8.	FIRE	* * * *	LIME
9.	FIRE	* * * *	REEL
10.	FLIP	* * * *	PONG

Elimination

The answers to the twelve questions are found by pairing off twenty-four of the twenty-five words. You will have one word over.

1. Be careful when opening the front door.
2. Tree used for tossing the caber?
3. Feline impressionist.
4. Room with sombre decoration for quiet thought.
5. Find the solution in the mausoleum?
6. Necessary in a dual instrument aeroplane.
7. Ideal craft for a party?
8. Surely these crustaceans are not used in snooker?
9. Difficult for them to keep dry?
10. Idiot's headgear made of paper?
11. Not a professional racing animal.
12. Doesn't take very long to eat this meat dish.

Select from

1. Brown	13. Hobby
2. Boat	14. House
3. Cat	15. Horse
4. Clue	16. Jolly
5. Copy	17. Minute
6. Cryptic	18. Pitch
7. Cap	19. Potted
8. Fools	20. Pine
9. Fish	21. Study
10. Flying	22. Steak
11. Fellow	23. Shrimps
12. Wet	24. Traveller
	25. Tree

Countries

Solution 22

Many words can be broken down into several smaller words. For example, contained within the seven-letter word 'forbear' are the words 'for', 'or', 'orb', 'be', 'bear' and 'ear'.

Can you find a seven-letter word which not only contains the name of a country but also the commonly used initials of two further countries?

Hexwords

Fit these words into the six spaces around each black centre, either clockwise or anti-clockwise so that all the words link up.

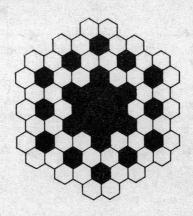

MISTED
REPORT
TERROR
LOFTED
DEMONS
SILVER
RIDERS
PORTER
MARROW
HOVERS
SNORES
MELLOW

Logic

Find the next figure in this sequence:

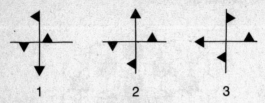

Choose from:

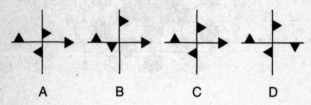

Square

Divide the square into four identical sections. Each section must contain the same nine letters, which can be arranged into a familiar nine-letter word.

O	P	C	H	T	G
T	H	R	I	Y	H
C	I	P	O	O	Y
G	Y	G	T	C	I
R	C	T	P	G	P
Y	H	I	R	O	R

Double Crossword

Place the words into crosswords. The crosswords have been mixed up.

NOG	HERO	ATOMS	ESTIMATOR
ERA	DEER	TAMED	SHELDRAKE
BUS	RISE	EMEND	SQUALIDLY
OAT	ROAR	NIGHT	VINDICATE
TOO	ALUM	APART	DESTROYER
EMU	PLEA	EVADE	ENDLESSLY
ARM	TRUE	REBID	STEEPNESS
ANY	EARL	ATOLL	VENERATED
	TOPS		
	EARN		
	DATE		
	IDOL		
	IOTA		
	ARTS		
	PAIR		
	RASP		

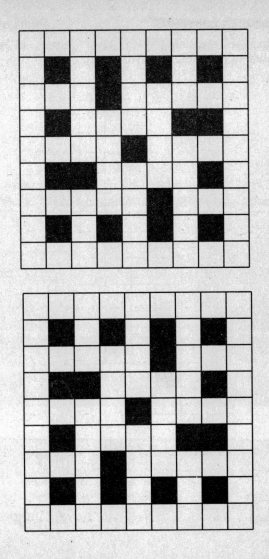

Alphabet Crossword

Fill in the remaining twenty-two letters of the alphabet to complete the crossword.

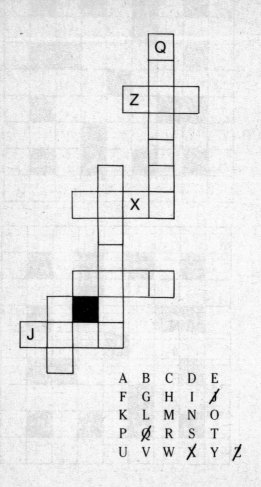

Odd One Out

Solution 56

Which is the odd one out?

ASS
CARESS
EXPRESS
HISS
NEEDLESS

Word Search

Solution 72

Find the names of fifteen card games. They read across, down, diagonally, backwards and forwards and always in a straight line.

S	B	E	T	E	U	Q	C	I	P
O	A	R	E	R	H	C	U	E	U
L	C	E	N	T	S	O	L	O	B
I	C	K	G	I	R	L	O	E	A
T	A	N	O	A	I	A	Z	Y	T
A	R	A	O	R	B	I	C	D	S
I	A	B	D	O	Q	B	N	E	A
R	T	A	Y	U	U	L	I	I	N
E	U	R	E	K	O	P	G	R	A
Q	P	I	N	O	C	L	E	B	C

Find Another Word

1. Consider the following list of words:
   SHADE, CLUB, JAR, CAP
   Now choose one of the following words to add to
   the list:
   LONG, JAM, CHARM, ROAD, WHITE

2. Consider the following list of words:
   NET, GO, MINE, NATION
   Now choose one of the following words to add to
   the list:
   PASS, FAT, FISH, PET, TIME

3. Consider the following list of words:
   BY, TO, OF, AFTER
   Now choose one of the following words to add to
   the list:
   AT, PASS, UPON, SO, WHY

Knight's Move

Solution 52

Start at 'B' and by knight moves spell out a quotation by H.W. Longfellow.

START

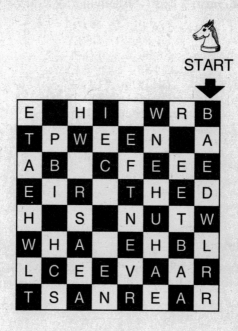

Hyphenated Words

Solution 9

These segments are all extracted from the middle of hyphenated words. You have to find the words.

Example: NT-BL – POINT-BLANK.

OW-BL	ND-RA
FT-HA	DE-EY
SS-PR	EG-PU
FT-SP	D'S-EY
GH-PO	UL-SE
UE-LI	OD-TE
EE-SH	AR-SI
W'S-HA	CE-OV
FF-NE	ND-PI
IE-HA	OW-MI

Division

Solution 11

Arrange the following digits 1–2–3–4–5–6–7–8–9 to form a single fraction that equals one quarter.

Blanks

Solution 4

This crossword has letters where the blanks should
be. Fill in the blanks to make the crossword read
correctly.

J	U	M	B	L	E	S	R	E	S	C	A	R
E	R	E	A	I	S	L	E	T	T	O	W	E
S	N	A	R	L	S	I	S	H	E	L	L	S
T	A	G	E	T	A	T	T	Y	S	L	A	T
E	A	R	C	R	Y	E	S	E	T	A	M	E
S	T	E	A	M	A	W	C	P	A	R	E	D
L	O	A	S	A	C	A	H	A	M	A	T	O
E	M	P	T	Y	A	V	A	R	E	F	E	R
U	S	E	S	A	B	I	T	I	S	I	R	E
R	A	P	E	C	O	M	E	T	E	A	V	A
O	R	P	H	A	N	I	L	A	S	S	O	S
P	I	E	A	R	E	A	L	M	A	C	A	P
E	D	D	Y	O	D	E	S	P	O	O	K	S

105

Zoetrope

Solution 107

Find a three-letter word in the outer scale which will also give a three-letter word in the inner scale. Then find a four-letter word in both scales; and a five-letter word. The same letter may be used twice. For example, the letters NUB on the outer scale spell GNU on the inner scale.

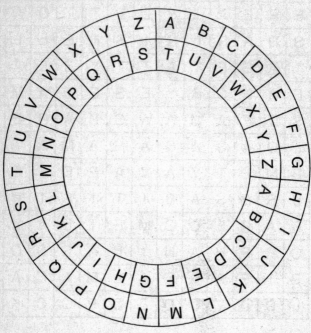

Choice

Each number has a choice of three letters. Select the correct letters.

2	2	2	4	■	■	7	7	1	1
4	1	8	■	1	■	5	6	2	
1	6	7	■	1	3	6	2	2	
9	■	6	■	4	■	■	■	5	
■	5	1	4	1	3	7	2	■	
7	■	■	5	■	2	■	1		
7	5	5	3	1	■	2	5	5	
1	8	2	■	2	■	1	5	7	
1	2	7	7	■	4	5	2	2	

1	A	B	C
2	D	E	F
3	G	H	I
4	J	K	L
5	M	N	O
6	P	Q	R
7	S	T	U
8	V	W	X
9	Y	Z	

Square
Solution 60

Divide the square into four parts of equal size and
shape. Each shape must include one of each of the
four symbols.

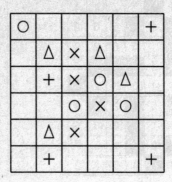

Rhyming Pairs
Solution 135

The answers to each of the following clues are a
rhyming pair of words, e.g. unhappy young man –
answer: SAD LAD.

1. Conceited horse race rider
2. Soviet beanbag
3. Principal sewage channel
4. Precise piece of information
5. Slightly drunk romany
6. Think highly of accoutrements
7. Irritate lad
8. Cherish free time
9. Culinary publication
10. Uncommon duo

Magic Square

Solution 92

Re-arrange the eighteen pairs of letters to form a magic square. Words read the same across and down.

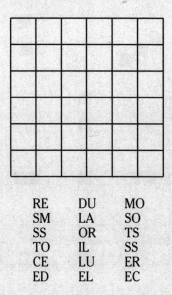

RE	DU	MO
SM	LA	SO
SS	OR	TS
TO	IL	SS
CE	LU	ER
ED	EL	EC

The Birthday Paradox

Solution 54

One evening, in a restaurant, there are twenty-four customers seated at tables. The probability that two of these customers, chosen at random, share the same birthday is one in 365, or 364 to 1, because (disregarding leap years) there are 365 days in a year. However, what are the odds that *any* two of the twenty-four people seated in the restaurant share the same birthday?

Crossword Fill-in

Place the 3 × 3 sets in the grid to complete the crossword.

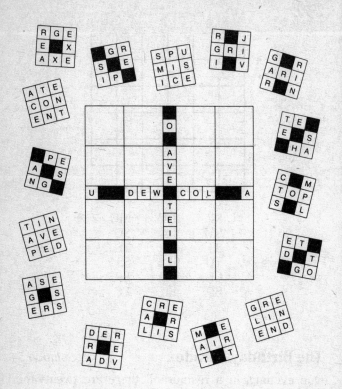

Word Construction

Use all the thirty small words scattered below once each only to construct ten words (three small words per word).

SON FEAT GALE ⬚⬚⬚⬚⬚⬚⬚⬚⬚⬚⬚

TEN ON ⬚⬚⬚⬚⬚⬚⬚

IN RING TAR ⬚⬚⬚⬚⬚⬚⬚⬚⬚

DANCE SPA ⬚⬚⬚⬚⬚⬚⬚⬚

ERA SEA TIN ⬚⬚⬚⬚⬚⬚⬚

HER BRAIN AT ⬚⬚⬚⬚⬚⬚⬚⬚

TOR ABLE ⬚⬚⬚⬚⬚⬚⬚⬚⬚⬚

AGE GOT BAD ⬚⬚⬚⬚⬚⬚⬚⬚

HER TEN NEW — ⬚⬚⬚⬚⬚⬚⬚⬚

MAR BONE BE ⬚⬚⬚⬚⬚⬚⬚⬚

RAG PER IMP ⬚⬚⬚⬚⬚⬚⬚⬚⬚⬚⬚

Middle Words

Fill in the missing word which, when tacked on to the first word, forms a new word and, when placed in front of the second word, forms another word.

1. GO . . . . . BACK (5)
2. GRID . . . . WARE (4)
3. MID . . . AWAY (3)
4. OFF . . . BOX (3)
5. PASS . . . . END (4)
6. OVER . . . PAYER (3)
7. UP . . . . TABLE (4)
8. CUT . . . . BITE (4)
9. BALL . . . . MATE (4)
10. TEA . . . ASH (3)
11. CAN . . . DID (3)
12. MASS . . . . AGE (4)
13. AIR . . . . AGE (4)
14. GUN . . . . . LESS (5)
15. PAPER . . . . BOARD (4)

Magic Squares

Ten words have been mixed up. Find out which words go into which grid and fit them in. The words read the same across and down.

ELUDE
ERODE
HOMES
MELON
OPERA
SANER
SPENT
STEWS
TULIP
WIDEN

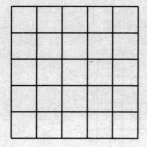
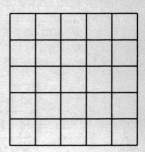

Letter Search

Consider the grid. Now answer these questions:

1. What letter comes just above the letter just before the letter just under the letter just under the letter just before the letter 'E'?

2. What letter comes just before the letter just above the letter just before the letter just below the letter which comes mid-way between the letters 'I' and 'A'?

3. What letter comes just above the letter just above the letter just after the letter just below the letter just after the letter just below the letter just below the letter 'S'?

4. What letter comes just under the letter just after the letter just after the letter just above the letter just above the letter which comes mid-way between the letters which come just below the letter 'R' and just above the letter 'A'?

P	J	C	N	E
B	S	Q	V	K
R	H	I	M	G
F	W	O	U	T
X	D	Y	L	A

Target

Pair up the thirty-two three-letter sections to form
sixteen six-letter words.

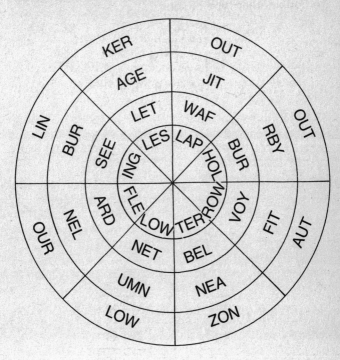

Music and Song

Complete the following which are all music and song.
Then arrange the first letters of each of the six words
to find another type of song.

    * R * A
    * U * L * B *
    * N * H * M
    * I * T *
    * A * C * R * L *
    * I * T

Word Circles

A) Place the letters in the correct boxes in each quadrant to obtain two eight-letter words, one reading clockwise and the other anti-clockwise. The two words are synonyms.

NW: PRLO   SW: IULH
NE: SIMI   SE: THEC

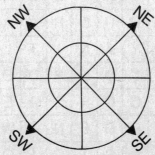

B) Place the letters in the correct boxes in each quadrant to obtain two eight-letter words, one reading clockwise and the other anti-clockwise. The two words are antonyms.

NW: RASE   SW: ELDB
NE: PESS   SE: SIME

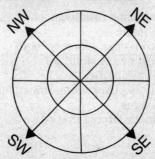

Word Power

The answers to the clues are to be found in the grid in letter order. They are all nine-letter words.

Example: Frozen (clue) is CRYOGENIC.

T	F	T	C	T	Q	O	M	W
A	O	R	U	O	R	V	A	A
A	N	Y	A	N	I	T	L	A
S	C	L	D	O	P	D	F	P
A	I	O	O	H	S	A	E	G
E	R	R	R	F	N	T	W	Z
O	M	N	G	I	O	I	O	I
A	O	E	I	U	E	L	A	R
E	D	S	L	D	C	L	D	L

1. Fantastic ornament
2. Ill made
3. Producing young by eggs
4. Reached a standard
5. Of the barber
6. Phrase expressing principles
7. Fungus
8. Quadrilateral shaped

118

Letter Omission

Solution 95

The answers to each pair of clues are two words which differ by omitting one letter only. Example: GUN/CHURCHMAN (6/5). Answer: CANNON/CANON.

1. UNIVERSAL/HUMOROUS (6/5)
2. PUT UP WITH/AN ASSISTANT (5/4)
3. FRAGRANCE/SULLEN (5/4)
4. PRIVATE/ASSUMED ROLE (8/7)
5. MEETING PLACE/LOOK HIGH AND LOW (5/4)
6. STARE ANGRILY/TAKE DOWN (6/5)
7. BANQUET/RAPID (5/4)
8. MUTILATE/CORNER (6/5)
9. DEDUCE/STEER (6/5)
10. DULL/CEREMONY (5/4)

Magic Square

Solution 141

Insert the numbers 1–25 to form a magic square where each horizontal, vertical and corner-to-corner line totals 65. Numbers 8 and 24 are already positioned.

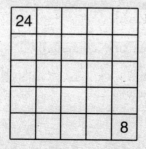

Labyrinth

Travel into each room once only to spell out a fifteen-letter word. You may move into the corridor as many times as you wish and you may start in any room, but you may visit each room only once.

120

Pair-words

Pair a word from list A with a word from list B until you have eight pairs. There are two possible pairing words in list A for each word in list B and vice versa. There are two correct solutions.

List A	List B
Pitch	Toss
Pike	Axe
Yarborough	Ship
Cutter	River
Canal	Whist
Castle	Moat
Hand	Prehensile
Tail	Earl

Clueless Crossword

In each square are four letters. Your task is to cross out three of each four, leaving one letter in each square, so the crossword is made up in the usual way with interlocking words.

T E	R O	E N	D O	P D	R V	O T
S C	E H	A T	C A	A R	U E	M E
E A		O R		R E		T I
L R		A U		A B		A O
Q E	T U	P M	Q A	A U	A C	E S
I A	X O	E T	T R	I N	E T	S M
R T		E N		T R		T S
U S		S I		E A		E A
T A	T I	S D	O R	R T	E S	R N
P J	C H	Q E	G U	A E	N O	E T

Word Circle

In the small circle below the words 'oncost', 'stripe' and 'person' are arranged clockwise, each overlapping by two letters. From the eight clues given opposite, *which are listed in order of difficulty, rather than in their correct order round the circle,* find eight six-letter words which, when placed in the correct order round the large circle, in a clockwise direction, will each overlap by two letters as shown in the example.

123

1. Mass of knotted fibres.
2. Make formal withdrawal from political alliance.
3. An inadequate amount.
4. Moderate to dark red colour.
5. Ball game played in France, Spain etc.
6. Messenger or envoy.
7. Hamlet, village.
8. Best and third best (in cards).

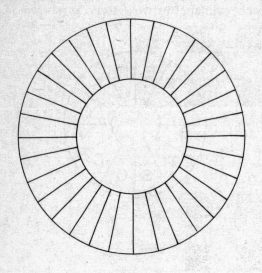

Choice Crossword

Solution 97

Each number has a choice of three letters. Select the correct letters.

6	2	1	3	7	2	2
2		1		5		3
2	7	6	4	5	5	3
7		1		4		2
7	5	2	2	2	2	7
2		2		6		7
2	3	7	7	7	2	7

1	A	B	C
2	D	E	F
3	G	H	I
4	J	K	L
5	M	N	O
6	P	Q	R
7	S	T	U
8	V	W	X
9	Y	Z	

Amoebas

Solution 70

An amoeba reproduces by dividing into two every minute. Two amoebas in a test tube can fill it to capacity in two hours. How long would one amoeba take to fill the same test tube?

Alphabet Crossword

Solution 16

Fill in the remaining twenty-one letters of the alphabet to complete the crossword.

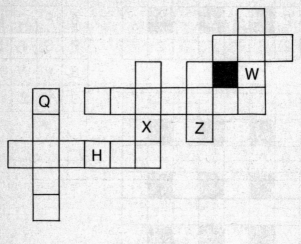

A B C D E
F G H̶ I J
K L M N O
P Q̶ R S T
U V W̶ X̶ Y Z̶

Piecemeal Quotation

A quotation has been divided up into three-letter groups and arranged in alphabetical order.

For example: 'Find the quote' would be presented: (4–3–5) DTH, EQU, FIN, OTE.

Now find this quotation by Washington Irving. (1–4–6–5–7–4–3–3–1–5–6–2–3–4–5–4–4–5–6–4–8–3).

AGE, AND, ANT, ARP, ASH, ATA, EDG, EDT, EMP, ERN, EVE, GUE, HCO, HEO, IST, ITH, KEE, LLO, NER, NLY, NST, OOL, OWS, RME, RTT, TGR, THA, TON, USE, WIT, WSW.

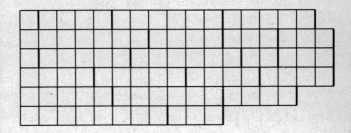

Elimination

The answers to the twelve questions are found by pairing off twenty-four of the twenty-five words. You will have one word over.

1. Mechanical object shaped like an insect.
2. Sounds as though the public transport has taken the wrong turning.
3. Demolition worker at a country house?
4. Would he need a sloping lake?
5. Sounds as though the bank-notes have been dropped in the sewer.
6. Sounds like an instrument to the removal men at the racecourse.
7. Another name for the space probe.
8. Bird with a crew-cut.
9. Animal anxious to get on building his dam.
10. Gent on a luxury cruise?
11. Charge for stealing the cutlery?
12. Short trousers for a dog?

Select from

1. Bill	13. Eagle
2. Bald	14. Horse
3. Butterfly	15. Nut
4. Blunder	16. Ocean
5. Beaver	17. Pack
6. Buss	18. Lucre
7. Boxer	19. Skier
8. Crashing	20. Spoon
9. Eager	21. Swell
10. Filthy	22. Shorts
11. Gate	23. Star
12. Green	24. Trek
	25. Water

Double Meanings

Solution 104

Which two words in the English language are synonyms when used as verbs but antonyms when used as adjectives, adverbs or nouns?

Odd One Out

Solution 99

Which is the odd one out?

HER
PIN
TAR
JUT
PAD
BID

Hexwords

Fit these words into the six spaces around each black centre, either clockwise or anti-clockwise so that all the words link up.

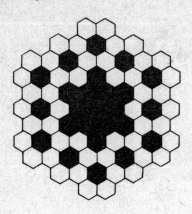

CARATS
RECORD
STUCCO
CAMBER
AROUND
ROBUST
ACCEPT
ATTACK
NUMBER
TREPAN
PANAMA
STRAPS

Choice

Each number has a choice of three letters. Select the correct letters.

3	3	6	2	■	8	1	3	7
1	6	2	■	2	■	8	2	2
4	2	2	3	2	■	1	7	2
4	■	■	1	4	1	6	■	6
■	5	3	7	■	4	2	3	■
6	■	5	2	7	7	■	■	1
2	6	1	■	7	5	8	2	4
7	5	3	■	9	■	5	2	7
7	7	2	8	■	7	5	7	5

1	A	B	C
2	D	E	F
3	G	H	I
4	J	K	L
5	M	N	O
6	P	Q	R
7	S	T	U
8	V	W	X
9	Y	Z	

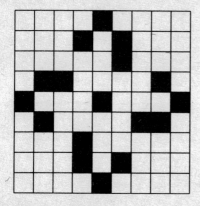

All Change

What comes next in this sequence?

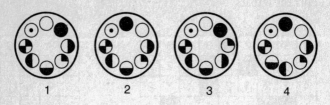

Choose from:

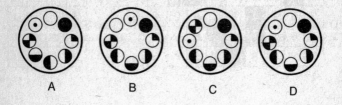

SOLUTIONS

1. Fours

page 92

1. Work
2. Dust
3. Ring
4. Crow
5. Back
6. Over
7. Star
8. Bird
9. Hose
10. Ping

2. Square

page 27

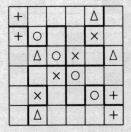

3. Odd One Out

page 23

(EVE)RYTHING: it contains a lady's name. All the others contain men's names.

CUS(TOM)ER
PROFIT(LES)S
ORIGIN(AL)
AS(SID)UOUS

4. Blanks

page 105

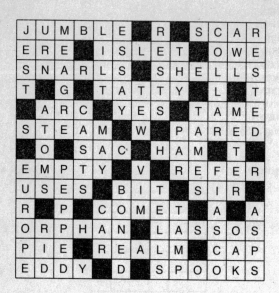

5. Alphabet Crossword

page 42

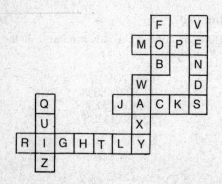

6. Elimination

page 93

1. Tree-house
2. Pitch pine
3. Copy-cat
4. Brown-study
5. Cryptic clue
6. Fellow traveller
7. Jolly boat
8. Potted shrimps
9. Wet fish
10. Foolscap
11. Hobby-horse
12. Minute-steak

ANSWER: FLYING

7. Fours

page 34

1. Like
2. Back
3. Fold
4. Rose
5. Head
6. Time
7. Roof
8. Mate
9. Coat
10. Worm

8. Knight's Move

page 23

'Looking on the happy autumn fields, and thinking of the days that are no more.'

– Tennyson

START

9. Hyphenated Words

page 104

Snow-blind
Left-handed
Mass-produce
Soft-spoken
High-powered
True-life
Tee-shirt
Jew's-harp
Stiff-necked
Die-hard

Second-rate
Wide-eyed
Leg-pull
Bird's-eye
Soul-searching
Good-tempered
Near-sighted
Voice-over *or* Once-over
Hand-pick
Narrow-minded

10. Keywords

page 34

1. GALLANTRY
2. MATERIAL

11. Division

page 104

$$\frac{3942}{15768}$$

12. Pyramid

page 21

Aga, aura, arena, angora, algebra, ambrosia, auditoria, acrophobia.

13. Double Crossword

page 63

14. Magic Square

page 91

S	T	R	I	P
T	H	A	N	E
R	A	B	A	T
I	N	A	N	E
P	E	T	E	R

15. Eiffel Tower

page 29

300 metres.

Let x equal height of Eiffel Tower.
Then height = $150 + \frac{1}{2}x$
$$x = 150 + \tfrac{1}{2}x$$
$$\tfrac{1}{2}x = 150$$
$$x = 300$$

16. Alphabet Crossword

page 126

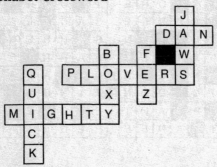

17. Colours

page 31

Saffron, olive, indigo, lime, sepia, orange, amber, peach, lilac.

18. Fore

page 87

Arm, bear, cast, castle, close, court, father, finger, front, go, gone, ground, hand, head, land, leg, lock, man, mast, most, see, sight, stall, tell, warn, word.

19. Pathway

page 28

Xiphoid
Xylonite
Xylophone
Xebec
Xanthoma
Xystus
Xylene
Xanthic

20. Inflation?

page 89

1990 × £0.50 = £995.00
1989 × £0.50 = £994.50

21. Word Power

page 118

1. Fandangle
2. Malformed
3. Oviparous
4. Qualified
5. Tonsorial
6. Watchword
7. Toadstool
8. Trapezial

22. Countries

page 94

Perusal — Peru, U.S.A., S.A.

23. Something in Common
page 18

They are all rivers in England.

24. Acrostic
page 13

'Love and a cottage, eh Fanny? Ah! Give me indifference and a coach an' six.'

George Colman

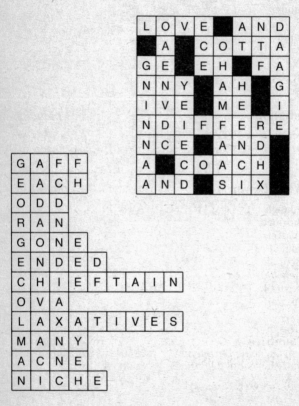

25. Choice

page 86

R	E	F	U	S	E	D
E	■	I	■	T	■	E
T	I	S	S	U	E	S
I	■	T	■	D	■	I
R	O	U	N	D	E	R
E	■	L	■	E	■	E
S	L	A	N	D	E	R

26. 6 × 6 Magic Square

page 30

S	T	E	E	D	S
T	U	R	R	E	T
E	R	R	A	T	A
E	R	A	S	E	R
D	E	T	E	S	T
S	T	A	R	T	S

27. Logic

page 6

C.

28. Words

page 44

Beaten: So that the remaining words start and finish with
consecutive letters of the alphabet, i.e.

Aplom**B**, **C**ar**D**, **E**l**F**, **G**rap**H**.

29. Connections

page 88

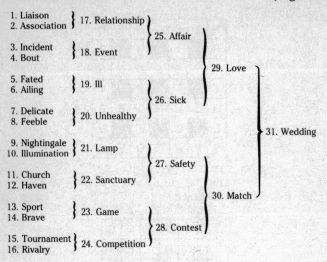

1. Liaison
2. Association } 17. Relationship

3. Incident
4. Bout } 18. Event

25. Affair

5. Fated
6. Ailing } 19. Ill

7. Delicate
8. Feeble } 20. Unhealthy

26. Sick

29. Love

9. Nightingale
10. Illumination } 21. Lamp

11. Church
12. Haven } 22. Sanctuary

27. Safety

31. Wedding

13. Sport
14. Brave } 23. Game

30. Match

15. Tournament
16. Rivalry } 24. Competition

28. Contest

30. Knight's Move

page 59

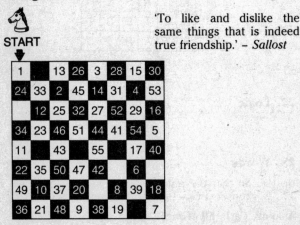

START

'To like and dislike the same things that is indeed true friendship.' – *Sallost*

1		13	26	3	28	15	30
24	33	2	45	14	31	4	53
	12	25	32	27	52	29	16
34	23	46	51	44	41	54	5
11		43		55		17	40
22	35	50	47	42		6	
49	10	37	20		8	39	18
36	21	48	9	38	19		7

144

31. Missing Letters
page 84

1. Shortbread
2. Gingerbread
3. Scone
4. Flan
5. Tart
6. Pie
7. Patty
8. Pasty
9. Doughnut
10. Turn-over

32. Choice
page 47

33. Book Titles
page 85

1. Enthral
2. Unmanly
3. Recreant
4. Skinhead
5. Eldest
6. Radiant
7. Glucose
8. Decrepit
9. Ukelele
10. Sideshow
11. Namesake
12. Breathless
13. General
14. Elapse
15. Formidable
16. Garden

34. Logic
page 39

B.

35. Common Clues
page 46

They all begin with the names of animals:

1. Pigment
2. Bulldozer
3. Assist
4. Dogfight
5. Catastrophe
6. Coward
7. Apex
8. Deerstalker
9. Sheepish
10. Camellia.

36. Anagrammed Synonyms
page 62

1. Club – Truncheon
2. Close – Imminent
3. Scorn – Derision
4. Dish – Platter
5. Rim – Border
6. Empty – Deserted
7. Home – Residence
8. Order – Arrangement
9. Cut – Lacerate
10. Stop – Terminate
11. Nude – Disrobed
12. Ape – Parody
13. Item – Article
14. Mar – Impair

37. Labyrinth
page 43

Flibbertigibbet.

38. Target
page 77

Cymbal	Feudal
Drogue	Nutmeg
Hyphen	Noddle
Indigo	Nearby
Devout	Ormulo
Bleach	Lagoon
Canned	Loosen
Fennel	Owlish

39. Word Search

page 58

L	I	C	E	Y	D	B	T	E	E
E	M	N	L	E	E	U	U	C	L
Z	P	L	O	E	N	W	L	U	P
A	O	D	C	T	I	C	I	R	A
H	A	H	S	L	P	L	P	P	M
R	S	E	L	M	O	L	I	S	B
Z	H	O	R	N	B	E	A	M	C
C	W	I	A	L	I	M	E	N	E
P	F	M	N	K	U	O	I	U	E
O	R	A	N	G	E	N	L	T	H

Tulip   Lime
Willow   Ash
Hornbeam   Elm
Chestnut   Pine
Beech   Spruce
Deodar   Lemon
Hazel   Orange
Holly   Nut
Gum   Maple
Fir   Plane
Oak

40. Spherical 1

page 12

Parenthesis   (Bracket)
Heinous   (Atrocious)
Edacious   (Gluttonous)
Riches   (Wealth)
Imperious   (Authoritative)
Callous   (Unfeeling)
Amass   (Accumulate)
Ludicrous   (Absurd)

41. Anagrams
page 45

1. Venus de Milo
2. Ronald Reagan
3. California
4. Carthorse
5. Sahara Desert

42. Three Words
page 36

They are each made up of consecutive letters of the alphabet.

43. Acrostic
page 37

'Oh! no man knows through what wild centuries roves back the rose, all that's past.'

Walter de la Mare

AUTHOR

44. Pyramid *page 57*

Congratulations.

45. Sequence *page 44*

Vacant: Each word begins with the initials of the colours of the rainbow: red, orange, yellow, green, blue, indigo, violet.

46. Pair-words *page 84*

Twig – Tree – Palm
Palm – Date – Calendar
Calendar – Month – Moon
Moon – Planet – Pluto
Pluto – Mickey – Mouse
Mouse – Trap – Gin
Gin – Rum – Sugar
Sugar – Cane – Twig

47. Overlapping Words *page 41*

Thirteenth, strategist, antipodean, entitlement, enthralment.

48. Sequence *page 58*

FY. (FIFTY). The sequence is the first and last letters of the value of current British coins.

49. Alphabet Crossword page 89

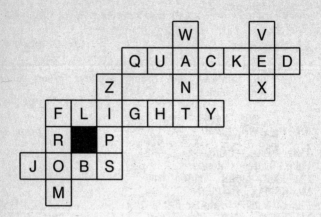

50. Pyramid Quotation page 54

I, GO, TRY, TINT, PETIT, SCHEME, SPINNER, EXCAVATE.

51. Odd One Out page 43

EQUATION: the others contain the five vowels A,E,I,O,U in the correct forward or reverse order.

52. Knight's Move

page 103

'Beware the pine tree's withered branch, beware the awful avalanches.'

— H.W. Longfellow

START

34		22	11		43	24	1
21	10	35	38	23	12		42
36	33		53	44	25	2	13
9	20	37		39	54	41	26
32		56		52	45	14	3
19	8	51		55	40	27	46
50	31	6	17	48	29	4	15
7	18	49	30	5	16	47	28

53. Vowels

page 51

Sequoia – Either of two giant Californian coniferous trees, the Redwood or Giant Sequoia.

54. The Birthday Paradox

page 109

54 in 100, or slightly better than half!

Calculation $\dfrac{364}{365} \times \dfrac{363}{365} \dots\dots\dots\dots \dfrac{342}{365} = \dfrac{46}{100}$

This figure is the probability that there will be no two people sharing the same birthday. The probability, therefore, that two people at least will match is $\dfrac{54}{100}$.

151

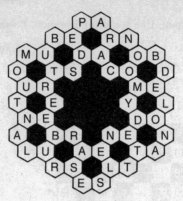

PARADE	DONATE	NEBULA
RACOON	NETTLE	TUREEN
BOOMED	LEASES	TUMOUR
MELODY	BURSAR	DEBUTS

56. Odd One Out

Express: In the others if you delete the final S you are left
with another word.

57. Elimination

1. Bandicoot
2. Gift-horse
3. Bogey-man
4. Bully-off
5. Freshman
6. Sandpiper
7. Witch hunt
8. Lantern-jawed
9. Night-watchman
10. Hedge-hopper
11. Monkey-puzzle
12. Penny-whistle

Answer: GOLLY

58. Alphabet Crossword
page 100

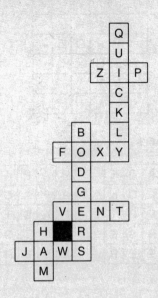

59. E-Frame
page 50

Across
1. Sextet
2. Even
3. Effect
4. Eleven
5. Essen
6. Mess
7. Teeter

Down
1. Select
2. Enter
3. Expel
4. Elect
5. Elevenses
6. Severe
7. Reference

60. Square

page 108

○					+
	△	×	△		
	+	×	○	△	
		○	×	○	
	△	×			
	+				+

61. Magic Squares

page 75

S	T	A	G	E
T	A	L	O	N
A	L	E	R	T
G	O	R	S	E
E	N	T	E	R

P	A	P	A	L
A	P	A	C	E
P	A	S	T	E
A	C	T	O	R
L	E	E	R	S

62. Choice

page 107

F	E	E	L		S	T	A	B
L	A	X		B		O	R	E
A	R	T		A	G	R	E	E
Y		R		L				N
	M	A	L	A	I	S	E	
S				N		E		A
T	O	N	I	C		D	O	N
A	W	E		E		A	N	T
B	E	T	S		K	N	E	E

154

63. Square Words

page 49

Cafeteria, bamboozle, overwhelm, reprehend, appliance.

64. Word Circle

page 80

Erotic, icecap, apathy, hybrid, idiocy, cypher, ermine, nether

65. Word Search

page 46

First.

66. Word Power

page 81

1. Truncheon
2. Maelstrom
3. Parbuckle
4. Snowstorm
5. Offensive
6. Horseplay
7. Ichthyoid
8. Gabionade

67. Choice

page 79

68. Addition

$$786.47$$
$$38.29$$
$$4.682$$
$$18.5$$
───────
$$847.942$$

69. Anagram Theme

DOGS: POINTER (TIN ROPE)
    SPANIEL (LANE SIP)
    BASSET (BEST AS)
    SHEEPDOG (HOPS EDGE)
    AIRDALE (READ AIL)
    SEALYHAM (HEALS MAY)
    PEKINGESE (SPIKE GENE)

70. Amoebas

Two hours and one minute.

71. Prime Number

Nil. The sum of the digits 1—8 is thirty-six. When the sum of the digits of any number is divisible by nine then that number will always divide by nine and three. Which ever order the balls are drawn out the sum of the digits of the number formed will always be thirty-six, therefore the number will divide by at least nine and three exactly and cannot be a prime number.

156

72. Word Search

page 101

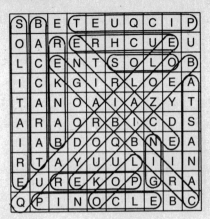

QUADRILLE
CRIBBAGE
CANASTA
SOLITAIRE
PICQUET
PINOCLE
BEZIQUE
BACCARAT

EUCHRE
ECARTE
POKER
LOO
GIN
BANKER
SOLO

73. Missing Letters

page 44

1. Watercourse
2. Streamlet
3. Spring
4. Fountain
5. Fount

6. Tributary
7. Brooklet
8. Gusher
9. Well
10. Waterway

74. Piecemeal Quotation

page 127

A tart temper never mellows with age and a sharp tongue is
the only edged tool that grows keener with constant use.

75. Word Search
page 22

```
D L I L A C M U E G
A C O W S L I P L O
I L W O T E N A Y R
S I L P E U D I S S
Y L S I R I L A N E
X Y P P O P U I A K
O N L L S E P L P C
L O I S E O I H E O
H E N O M E N A O T
P P O R C H I D N S
```

Gladioli	Orchid
Iris	Pansy
Rose	Geum
Aster	Lilac
Tulip	Anemone
Lupin	Cowslip
Dahlia	Phlox
Poppy	Daisy
Peony	Gorse
Lily	Stock

76. Elimination
page 128

1. Butterfly-nut
2. Blunder-buss
3. Gatecrashing
4. Water-skier
5. Filthy-lucre
6. Pack-horse
7. Star-trek
8. Bald-eagle
9. Eager-beaver
10. Ocean-swell
11. Spoon-bill
12. Boxer-shorts

Answer: GREEN

77. Spherical 2

page 73

Pertinacious	(Persistent)
Hapless	(Unlucky)
Embarrass	(Encumber)
Rumbustious	(Boisterous)
Incredulous	(Unbelieving)
Cantankerous	(Quarrelsome)
Annals	(Records)
Luminous	(Shining)

78. Grandpa's Party

page 29

My grandfather is seventy-two years old. I am twenty-two years old. Sixty grandsons received invitations.

79. Hexwords

page 19

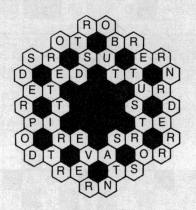

ROBUST	TERROR	TRIPOD
BUTTER	ROSTAS	PITTER
RETURN	TAVERN	DETERS
RUSTED	REVERT	STORED

80. Farmer Giles

page 20

One Cow
One Bull
Two Horses
One Chicken

81. Double Crossword

page 55

82. Cryptograms

page 20

1. If we were all given by magic the power to read each other's thoughts, I suppose the first effect would be to dissolve all friendships.

– Bertrand Russell.

2. He uses statistics as a drunken man uses a lamp post – for support rather than for illumination.

– Andrew Lang.

3. The attempt to combine wisdom and power has only rarely been successful and then only for a short while.

– Albert Einstein.

83. Cipher

page 74

Message successfully decoded, congratulations.

Add each group of three numbers together and take the corresponding letter in the alphabet.

84. Word Construction

page 111

Herringbone   Seasonable
Badinage   Attendance
Martingale   Imperator
Begotten   Tarragon
Newspaper   Featherbrain

85. Backwards and Forwards

page 18

The man walks for 9 miles at 4 m.p.h. which takes 2¼ hours.
The dog therefore runs for 2¼ hours at 9 m.p.h. and covers 20¼ miles.

86. Alphabet Crossword
page 48

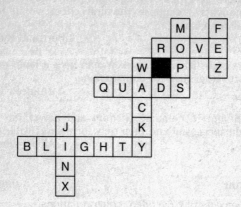

87. Pair-words
page 45

Golf – Slice – Fish
Fish – Nets – Cricket
Cricket – Match – Vesta
Vesta – Swan – Goose
Goose – Quill – Pen
Pen – Fountain – Gargoyle
Gargoyle – Spout – Teapot
Teapot – Caddy – Golf

88. Fours
page 74

1. Wind
2. Love
3. Over
4. Gate
5. Horn
6. Land
7. Pass
8. Sick
9. Worm
10. Hand

89. A-Frame
page 16

Across	**Down**
1. Astral	1. Crack
2. Avast	2. Manx
3. Arkansas	3. Park
4. Awkward	4. Alarm
5. Aghast	5. Amass
6. Ayah	6. Sand
7. Abyss	7. Appal

90. Division
page 51

$$\frac{3187}{25496}$$

91. Blanks
page 24

92. Magic Square

T	O	S	S	E	D
O	R	M	O	L	U
S	M	I	L	E	R
S	O	L	A	C	E
E	L	E	C	T	S
D	U	R	E	S	S

93. Word Power

1. Fricassee
2. Chinaware
3. Sepulchre
4. Freshener
5. Snakeskin
6. Rowdiness
7. Dividends
8. Arrowroot

94. All Change

C.

95. Letter Omission

1. COSMIC/COMIC
2. ABIDE/AIDE
3. ODOUR/DOUR
4. PERSONAL/PERSONA
5. HAUNT/HUNT
6. GLOWER/LOWER
7. FEAST/FAST
8. MANGLE/ANGLE
9. DERIVE/DRIVE
10. TRITE/RITE

96. Blanks

page 61

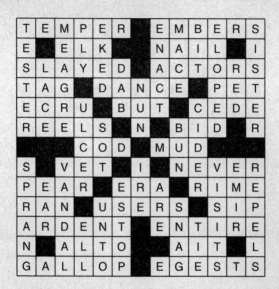

T	E	M	P	E	R		E	M	B	E	R	S
E		E	L	K			N	A	I	L		I
S	L	A	Y	E	D		A	C	T	O	R	S
T	A	G		D	A	N	C	E		P	E	T
E	C	R	U		B	U	T		C	E	D	E
R	E	E	L	S		N		B	I	D		R
		C	O	D		M	U	D				
S		V	E	T		I		N	E	V	E	R
P	E	A	R		E	R	A		R	I	M	E
R	A	N		U	S	E	R	S		S	I	P
A	R	D	E	N	T		E	N	T	I	R	E
N		A	L	T	O			A	I	T		L
G	A	L	L	O	P		E	G	E	S	T	S

97. Choice Crossword

page 125

R	E	C	I	T	E	D
E		A		O		I
F	U	R	L	O	N	G
U		A		L		E
T	O	F	F	E	E	S
E		E		R		T
D	I	S	U	S	E	S

98. Alphabet Crossword

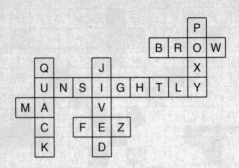

99. Odd One Out

Pad: The others can be made into a new word by adding an E to the end.

100. Square

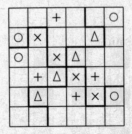

101. Target

page 15

Jocose	Sherry
Lacuna	Urchin
Lounge	Violet
Noggin	Tumour
Outcry	Torpid
Musket	Zombie
Jockey	Wiggle
Shalom	Whacky

102. Elimination

page 90

1. Gold-digger
2. Paddy-field
3. High-flyer
4. Glow-worm
5. Micro-chip
6. Crab-apple
7. Draw-bridge
8. Gobstopper
9. Cow-catcher
10. Day-dreamer
11. Beach-comber
12. Pussy-willow

Answer: STREAM

103. Zoetrope

page 65

3. LIP – AXE
4. CLAD – RAPS
5. DAZED – SPOTS

104. Double Meanings

page 129

Best and Worst.

105. Trios

page 18

Illgotten, pantryman, pentagram, redevelop, warrantor.

106. Zoetrope

3. RAN – IRE
4. CRAN – TIRE
5. BUNNY – SLEEP

107. Zoetrope

3. ALL – TEE
4. SPUN – LING
5. SHALY – LATER

108. Nines

4	7	3	2	2
8	9	6	1	3
1	4	3	4	6
2	1	3	1	2
3	6	3	1	5

Other solutions may be possible.

109. Pair-words

Yarborough – Whist – Hand
Hand – Prehensile – Tail
Tail – Toss – Pitch
Pitch – Ship – Cutter
Cutter – Axe – Pike
Pike – River – Canal
Canal – Moat – Castle
Castle – Earl – Yarborough

110. Choice
page 33

M	E	N	D	I	C	A	N	T
I		E		N		V		E
S	W	E	A	T		A	W	L
C			R	O	B	S		E
R	O	L	E		A	T	O	M
E		O	A	S	T			E
A	R	C		A	S	S	E	T
N		U		G		E		R
T	E	M	P	O	R	A	R	Y

111. Advanced Matrix
page 76

4.

112. Target Crossword
page 32

Abbess
Batman
Chichi
Gourde
Iguana
Ostler
Quince
Racoon

Raffle
Rosily
Sandal
Sennet
Vestry
Violet
Violin
Wombat

113. Clueless Crossword

page 122

C	O	N	C	A	V	E
L	█	O	█	B	█	A
A	T	T	R	A	C	T
S	█	E	█	T	█	E
P	I	D	G	E	O	N

114. Target

page 115

Outlet
Nearby
Linnet
Kernel
Jitter
Outfit
Lessee
Hollow

Zoning
Voyage
Waffle
Bellow
Autumn
Ardour
Burlap
Burrow

115. Choice

page 11

R	E	P	U	T	E	S
E	█	U	█	E	█	A
D	E	F	I	N	E	D
U	█	F	█	D	█	I
C	H	I	M	E	R	S
E	█	N	█	R	█	T
D	E	S	I	S	T	S

116. Choice

page 131

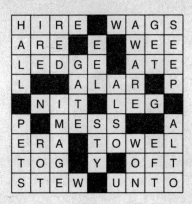

117. Middle Words

page 112

1. Sling
2. Iron
3. Get
4. Ice
5. Port
6. Tax
7. Turn
8. Back
9. Room
10. Pot
11. Can
12. Acre
13. Line *or* Port
14. Point
15. Clip

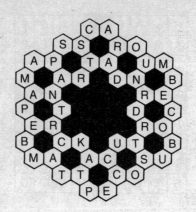

CARATS
AROUND
NUMBER
RECORD
ROBUST
STUCCO
ACCEPT
ATTACK
CAMBER
TREPAN
PANAMA
STRAPS

119. Crossword Fill In

page 110

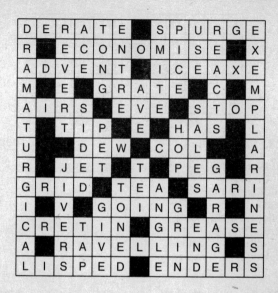

D	E	R	A	T	E		S	P	U	R	G	E
R		E	C	O	N	O	M	I	S	E		X
A	D	V	E	N	T		I	C	E	A	X	E
M		E		G	R	A	T	E		C		M
A	I	R	S		E	V	E		S	T	O	P
T		T	I	P		E		H	A	S		L
U		D	E	W		C	O	L			A
R		J	E	T		T		P	E	G		R
G	R	I	D		T	E	A		S	A	R	I
I		V		G	O	I	N	G		R		N
C	R	E	T	I	N		G	R	E	A	S	E
A		R	A	V	E	L	L	I	N	G		S
L	I	S	P	E	D		E	N	D	E	R	S

120. Word Circle

page 123

Tenace, cerise, secede, dearth, thorpe, pelota, tangle, legate.

121. Word Circles

page 117

A)   Churlish, Impolite.
B)   Disperse, Assemble.

122. Magic Squares

page 35

M	O	T	O	R
O	K	A	P	I
T	A	C	I	T
O	P	I	N	E
R	I	T	E	S

N	O	M	A	D
O	M	E	G	A
M	E	D	A	L
A	G	A	P	E
D	A	L	E	S

123. Pair-words

page 10

Sword – Stiletto – Foot
Foot – Stirrup – Saddle
Saddle – Lamb – Meat
Meat – Sweet – Toffee
Toffee – Apple – Core
Core – Sample – Try
Try – Rugby – Tackle
Tackle – Fish – Sword

124. Find Another Word

page 102

1. LONG: All words can be prefixed with 'night'.
2. PET: All words can be prefixed with 'car'.
3. UPON: All words can be prefixed with 'here' or 'there'.

125. Detective Work

page 85

Alf Grey.

126. Anagram Quotations

page 9

A – 2	SUNSHINE	E – 4	CONCENTRATED
B – 6	ADVERSITY	F – 1	FRIENDSHIP
C – 5	COMMENDATION	G – 3	ADMIRATION
D – 8	PREJUDICES	H – 7	PERPETUAL

127. Odd One Out
page 66

Prevent: the others have two pronunciations.

128. Numbers
page 78

Arrange them into groups each totalling 10,000.

5362/2981/1657,   3947/1444/4609,   7201/1012/1787,
3821/1649/4530.

129. 6 × 6 Magic Square
page 70

C	I	R	C	L	E
I	C	A	R	U	S
R	A	R	E	S	T
C	R	E	A	T	E
L	U	S	T	R	E
E	S	T	E	E	M

130. Magic Squares
page 113

H	O	M	E	S
O	P	E	R	A
M	E	L	O	N
E	R	O	D	E
S	A	N	E	R

S	T	E	W	S
T	U	L	I	P
E	L	U	D	E
W	I	D	E	N
S	P	E	N	T

131. Magic Word Square
page 8

T	O	D	A	Y
O	B	E	S	E
D	E	L	T	A
A	S	T	E	R
Y	E	A	R	N

132. Something In Common
page 27

They can all be prefixed with men's names to form another word: Jackass, Rayon, Tomboy, Bobbin, Nickname, Leeway.

133. No Repeat Letters
page 10

Ambidextrous.

134. Target
page 36

Polish	Tragic
Kibitz	Pocket
Oolite	Parole
Kitten	Plague
Pillow	Parang
Shimmy	Kewpie
Unseen	Iodine
Vacuum	Number

135. Rhyming Pairs
page 108

1. Cocky Jocky
2. Russian Cushion
3. Main Drain
4. Exact Fact
5. Tipsy Gypsy
6. Admire Attire
7. Annoy Boy
8. Treasure Leisure
9. Cook Book
10. Rare Pair

136. Square

page 4

Multitude.

U	E	T	U	D	I
D	T	M	E	M	L
T	U	I	U	T	T
U	E	L	T	M	U
T	U	D	T	D	I
M	I	L	U	E	L

137. Labyrinth

page 120

Pulchritudinous.

138. Square

page 97

Copyright.

O	P	C	H	T	G
T	H	R	I	Y	H
C	I	P	O	O	Y
G	Y	G	T	C	I
R	C	T	P	G	P
Y	H	I	R	O	R

139. End

page 35

One chance in 15,600, or 26 × 25 × 24.

140. Pathway

page 68

1. Vendetta
2. Velocity
3. Verona
4. Varicose
5. Vulpine
6. Viscosity
7. Vivid
8. Voted

141. Magic Square

page 119

24	6	12	5	18
13	10	17	9	16
11	7	1	25	21
3	23	15	22	2
14	19	20	4	8

142. Beads

page 69

A =

B =

To form a magic square, the number of beads 1–9 are positioned so that each horizontal, vertical and corner-to-corner line totals fifteen. The odd numbers are white dots and the even numbers black dots.

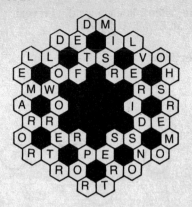

MISTED
SILVER
HOVERS
RIDERS
DEMONS
SNORES
REPORT
PORTER
TERROR
MARROW
MELLOW
LOFTED

1. Marijuana
2. Buffaloes
3. Paralysis
4. Fetishism
5. Quadratic
6. Desecrate
7. Threshold
8. Hopscotch

145. Coded Message

page 66

Take the letter after E in each word, to reveal
the message 'MEET ME TONIGHT'.

146. Connections

page 60

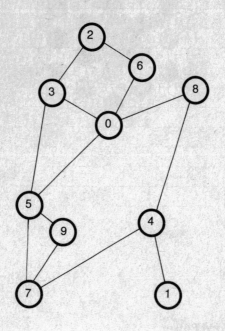

147. Logic

page 96

C.

148. Crossword Fill-in
page 72

C	H	A	S	T	E	░	S	T	A	R	E	D
O	░	R	E	I	N	S	T	A	T	E	░	I
S	T	O	N	E	S	░	A	G	E	N	T	S
M	░	M	░	S	U	I	T	S	░	D	░	C
O	P	A	L	░	E	V	E	░	P	E	E	R
P	░	S	E	W	░	Y	░	T	O	R	░	I
O	░	░	M	E	T	░	W	A	S	░	░	M
L	░	C	O	D	░	H	░	B	E	D	░	I
I	R	A	N	░	D	U	D	░	S	E	E	N
T	░	V	░	R	E	B	U	T	░	P	░	A
I	R	O	N	I	C	░	C	O	H	O	R	T
S	░	R	E	S	O	N	A	T	O	R	░	O
M	A	T	T	E	R	░	L	E	T	T	E	R

149. Letter Search
page 114

1. Q.
2. W.
3. M.
4. G.

150. Pathway
page 3

Zugzwang
Zoetrope
Zombie
Zeppelin
Zephyr
Zenith
Zygal
Ziggurats

151. Common Clues

page 82

They are all types of dance:
1. Barn   2. Twist   3. Tap   4. Folk   5. Square
6. Reel   7. Jig   8. War

152. Music and Song

page 116

Aria
Lullaby
Anthem
Ditty
Barcarole
Lilt

Anagram: BALLAD.

153. Double Crossword

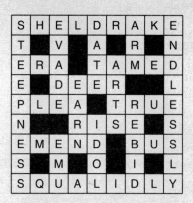

154. Labyrinth

Quadruplication.

155. Labyrinth

Trigonometrical.

156. Missing Letters

page 9

1. Partridge
2. Pheasant
3. Woodpigeon
4. Turkey
5. Goose
6. Woodcock
7. Duck
8. Grouse
9. Pullet
10. Capon

THE MENSA PUZZLE BOOK
Philip Carter & Ken Russell

This challenging collection of Mensa puzzles is not for the faint-hearted. You'll need all your wits about you to solve the dazzling range of brainteasers – crosswords, word and number games, grid and diagram puzzles – a veritable cornucopia of craftiness.

The ultimate quiz book for the ultimate quiz addict.

0 7474 0118 7
CROSSWORDS/QUIZZES

All Sphere Books are available at your bookshop or newsagent, or can be ordered from the following address: Sphere Books, Cash Sales Department, P.O. Box 11, Falmouth, Cornwall TR10 9EN.

Please send cheque or postal order (no currency), and allow 60p for postage and packing for the first book plus 25p for the second book and 15p for each additional book ordered up to a maximum charge of £1.90 in U.K.

B.F.P.O. customers please allow 60p for the first book, 25p for the second book plus 15p per copy for the next 7 books, thereafter 9p per book.

Overseas customers, including Eire, please allow £1.25 for postage and packing for the first book, 75p for the second book and 28p for each subsequent title ordered.